Beaufort Cottage "

Best wishes

Peter Rossdale

The History of Equine Veterinary Practice in Newmarket from 1831 to 2011

Edited by Peter Rossdale, Peter Jackson and Timothy Cox

Front cover
*Newmarket Clock Tower in centre around which, from top left to right, are:
1, String of horses at exercise beside Moulton Road. 2, Long Hill sand track.
3, Bob Crowhurst and Brayley Reynolds having just completed an operation.
4, Fred Day at Egerton Stud with mare and foal. 5, Newly born foal at Cheveley
Park Stud attended by Andrew Snell. 6, Examples of modern veterinary
practice (a. MRI image of foot with cyst present b. Rossdales Equine
Veterinary Hospital premises established 1998 c. View of larynx taken via
scope in place during exercise). 7, John Bowles and George Barrow
Newmarket vets of 19th century.*

Publisher's acknowledgements
*My sincere thanks to all the authors who kindly devoted time and effort in presenting
their chapters; and to Peter Jackson and Timothy Cox for their co-editorial
assistance. James Power and Trevor Jones contributed artwork
and photography as indicated in captions.
Kirsty Hopkin of Digital Print Services (EA) Ltd and Paul Hammond
prepared the text and illustrations for printing.*
Peter Rossdale, Director of Romney Publications Ltd

1

Chapters 1 & 10
Peter Rossdale
OBE PhD FRCVS

Chapter 6
Sir Mark Prescott
Bt

Chapter 2
Peter Jackson
MA FRCVS

Chapter 7
Sidney Ricketts
LVO FRCPath FRCVS

Chapter 3
Timothy Cox
MA

Chapter 7
Nicholas Wingfield Digby
BVSc MRCVS DL

Chapter 4
Alan Medlock

Chapter 8
Peter Webbon
DVR PhD MRCVS

Chapter 5
Richard Greenwood
MA Vet MB MRCVS

Chapter 9
Simon Curtis
FWCF Hon Assoc RCVS

Contents

Brough riding Red Rum outside the very visibly titled McCain's Car Sales one very wet morning in Southport, way back in 1975. Red Rum won the Grand National in 1973, 1974 and 1977. He also came second in the two intervening years. In addition to this unprecedented record in the world-famous steeplechase, Red Rum fell only once in over 100 races.

Donald McCain, better known as Ginger, applied for a training permit in 1953 and began training horses in 1962, using small stables behind the showroom of his used-car store in Southport. He bought a horse for 6,000 guineas, which later turned out to be suffering from a debilitating bone disease. The horse was Red Rum. He trained the winner of the Grand National four times, thrice with Red Rum and once with Amberleigh House, victories over 30 years apart. Fred Rimell is the only other person to have trained four winners of the race.

Brough Scott is a graduate of Oxford University He rode 100 winners as an amateur and professional jockey. For 30 years he presented the major races for ITV and Channel 4 Racing. As a journalist for the Sunday Times, Independent on Sunday and Sunday Telegraph he has three times been Sports Feature Writer of The Year. He contributes to the Racing Post which he founded with Sheikh Mohammed in 1986. Brough has written seven books, including 'World of Horse Racing in 1982' and 'Galloper Jack', the critically acclaimed biography of his grandfather. He is currently at work on a life of Sir Henry Cecil".

Preface

BROUGH SCOTT

Prepare to learn, prepare to laugh and prepare at times to nearly cry at the ignorance and pettiness which hindered progress for far too long. This book is an enterprise of both research and reconciliation. It reads not just like important local history but as a book of wider truth.

I never realised that vets were once thought of so poorly by both outsiders and each other. Peter Rossdale and his distinguished collaborators have held up the mirror and been unafraid to record the less pleasing as well as the quirkier reflections. They were right to do so because the journey of the veterinary profession in Newmarket from the mistrusted and poorly qualified past to the world leading service of today is unique both in achievement and location.

For Newmarket is where it all began. It has been the key place and inspiration in the development of the Thoroughbred racehorse into the fastest weight carrying creature that the world has ever seen and England's greatest gift to the animal kingdom. This book is a reminder of both the dark and the light, of the creative side of The Jockey Club and of racing's seamier undercurrents most graphically illustrated with the exploits of the horse poisoner Daniel Dawson who ended up swinging from the gallows in Cambridge in front of a 15,000 strong crowd.

But its greatest achievement is to link the more recent past with the infinitely more modern present, of the journey from dominant personalities and a mere 750 horses to today's seriously scientific based service with almost four times the patient numbers. No future compendium should be without Sir Mark Prescott's hilarious but insightful account of this period even if only for the description of the long reined yearling that bolted full on into a wall at Heath House - "a cloud of dust, like a small nuclear mushroom cloud, rose above his prostrate body - followed by a subsequent eerie silence."

Amazingly the yearling survived, albeit without his testicles. So too did Bob Cook survive but not without early days of handling a most basic form of endoscope which was little more than an adaption of the "borescope" used for inspecting gun barrels. Relish the understatement as he says: "the number of veterinarians, worldwide, who have used such an instrument could be counted on one hand with several fingers missing."

There have been times in the past when there has been a complacency in the claim that Newmarket was "The Home of the Thoroughbred" and these pages admit a long standing inter-practice "cold war" when Peter Rossdale broke the monopoly at Reynolds House and set up on his own. By bringing the whole tale together he has done more than unite a profession and justify that original Newmarket claim. He has done history a service.

Courtesy Trevor Jones.

Published by
Romney Publications Ltd
Romney House, Dullingham Road, Newmarket, Suffolk. CB8 9JU
www.romneypublications.co.uk

First edition September 2011

Designed and Typeset by
Digital Print Services (EA) Ltd & Paul Hammond

Printed by
Geerings Print Ltd, Ashford, Kent.

Chapter 1

Equine Veterinary Practice in Newmarket

by: Peter Rossdale OBE PhD FRCVS

*P**eter Rossdale chose to be a vet because of an early life passion for horses, riding and racing. He gained the Natural Science Tripos degree at Cambridge University in 1949 and then studied at the Royal Veterinary College (RVC) in Camden Town and Streatley before graduating as a Member of the Royal College Veterinary Surgeons (RCVS) in 1952. He entered the Rye general practice of Ron Ogle before moving to Newmarket, where he achieved a Fellowship of the RCVS by thesis and a PhD Cantab on the basis of published papers. He has received Honorary Doctorates from the Universities of Berne, Edinburgh and Sydney; and an Honorary Fellowship of the RVC in 2010. Photo: Dismounting Colonel Whitcomb's Maddox Street after winning at Tickham Point-to-Point. Note no helmet, only a detachable skull cap in those days!*

Intoduction

This book aims to provide an account of the development of veterinary services in Newmarket, UK over the past two centuries. Authors of chapters describe the range of such services as they exist today and their origins. A corresponding account is planned as a sequence of articles in Equine Veterinary Education in which members of the profession with particular expertise in their speciality outline the progress in veterinary medicine and surgery that has taken place over the past 50 years worldwide.

The Veterinarian 1831

The idea to record the history of veterinary practice in Newmarket was based upon an editorial in The Veterinarian of 1831. In this, the writer claimed that *"no veterinary surgeon had been able to obtain a living at Newmarket, this despite the fact that there are always a great number of valuable horses stabled there."* The writer observed that *"The horses are not only valuable in themselves, but their owners have staked immense fortunes upon them"*. Several of the contributors of the chapters that follow make reference to the comments contained in the editorial; and question the accuracy of the observations there recorded.

The article continued .....*"seven or eight young men have gone, one after the other, from the Veterinary College to Newmarket, and have left it in a year or two in despair. An old farrier residing there does considerable business; and Mr Bowles, of Cambridge, a very excellent practitioner,* *is frequently consulted; but a veterinary surgeon cannot live at Newmarket."*

The reason for this the author continued was that *"There are, however, some peculiarities about Newmarket, whatever might be our first impression, that are really unfavourable to the success of the veterinary practitioner. In the first place it is the metropolis of the groom's empire; it is where he has for many a year ruled with absolute sway, and where he would be most of all jealous of a rival, and a rival whose superiority he feels and dreads. In many stables the master is comparatively powerless: in the training-stable he is a mere cipher. The tyranny of the groom, founded, like tyranny everywhere, on ignorance and indolence, is despotic. Some masters submit to it reluctantly, but all do submit to it; and the management of the race-horse, in health and in sickness too, is the peculiar province of the training-groom"*

Of course, the above quotations were from an article written 180 years ago and reflect the prevailing social attitudes of the day, then subsequently to be portrayed by Charles Dickens concerning national arrogances.

The Horseman

Rivalries between experts are well-recognised in all walks of life. Members of professions zealously guard their reputations for efficiency, knowledge, wisdom and authority, not only between their colleagues, but even more from intrusion by outsiders into what they consider to be their special preserves. This concern is justifiable to a degree, since apprenticeship, experience and learning are not unique to those in a particular profession, but may be acquired by outsiders, as is customary in many trades.

There are many facets to the traditional and current contributions of the horse to the civilisation and pleasures of mankind. The horseman is recognised as someone who has a special affinity with this creature which has for many thousand years, been at our service to ride, race, pull carts or be used by troops in war. The horseman is a person skilled in the handling of the horse and has a natural, or learned understanding of the traits and behavioural quirks of each individual animal, together with the patience to persevere in its control and training.

Stud and Stable Staff

The increasing conclusion of the present writer, based upon 50 years of veterinary practice in Newmarket, has been the outstanding commitment of the individuals who handle and care for the horses in their charge on studfarms and in stables devoted to racing or riding.

Fred Peacock in the fifties at Cheveley Park Stud. A member of stud staff essential to vets in practice.

The term "groom" has a somewhat pejorative resonance of the past. Our profession depends for its medical and surgical expertise and success on those who handle our "patients"; and on their willingness to interpret and report on the symptoms they observe, both promptly and accurately. Their dedication throughout day and night is performed in parallel with their veterinarian and the importance of this close relationship cannot be over emphasised. Without co-operation

between vet and those who manage and handle horses, veterinary practice would not be possible to the high standard rightly expected of it.

The relationship has been fostered over the years by the courses of education now available via such as the Animal Health Trust (AHT), Thoroughbred Breeders Association (TBA) and National Stud and the Trainers Federation. Fifty years ago, there were few if any such courses. In the 1960s the present writer recalls informal meetings held in the evening in the sitting-up room at Cheveley Park stud. These were attended by a small band of stud and stable hands, enthusiastic for learning veterinary subjects. These meetings increased in size and moved to Foley House. The Derisley Wood Stud School was started in the 1970s under the auspices of the owner, Irving Allen a Californian film producer and with the support of the local MP, Eldon Griffiths. The concept of the school was then taken up and continued successfully by the National Stud.

Multi-membered Practices

There are now 3 equine veterinary practices in Newmarket. One was established in the early part of the last century (Chapters 5 and 6) and one in 1959 (Chapter 7).

Members of Hill House practice. l-r Paul Lentelink, Fernando Perez, Brian Abbot, Duncan Moir, Antony Clements

A third equine practice was started in Newmarket in September 2006 and known as Messrs. Baker, McVeigh & Clements Ltd. This practice is now based at Hill House, Falmouth Avenue, Newmarket. There are five veterinary surgeons in the practice and John McVeigh and Antony Clements are the two local partners. Some members of the practice have worked in South

Africa and originally came to Newmarket to attend horses with South African connections, that were stabled there for training. The practice provides an ambulatory service and does not currently have or plan an Equine Hospital. Horses requiring hospital treatment are referred to an equine hospital selected in discussion with their owners. Since then they have taken on the work at a number of other local yards. The practice works chiefly with racing stables and at the Newmarket sales.

What is a Profession?

Classically, there were only three professions, Divinity, Medicine and Law. The main milestones which marked such an occupation being identified as a profession were: a full-time occupation, a school or university in which undergraduates received training and, over time, the formation of Associations, development of codes of professional conduct and the establishment of national licensing laws.

With the rise of technology and occupational specialisation in the 19th century, other bodies began to claim professional status: such as Veterinary Medicine, Dentistry, Pharmacy, Nursing, Teaching etc.

Although professions enjoy high status and public prestige, not all professionals earn high salaries; and various peripheral elements of professional activity may readily be practised by individuals with no specific training or certification. This is evident in many walks of life but equally where horses are concerned, which is illustrated in the editorial in The Veterinarian 1831 and quoted above.

Chapters to Follow

Chapter one aims to set the scene for the central theme of the book, namely provision of veterinary services to the stud and stable population of horses in Newmarket in the interests of their welfare and their owners.

In Chapter 2, Peter Jackson, a distinguished veterinary educator and practitioner, outlines the history of veterinary education as it has developed, with particular emphasis on aspects relating to the horse. The veterinary profession is recognised in law and its members are accorded the privilege of practising the art and science of veterinary

medicine and surgery. This privilege is based upon the attainment of a high standard of education before entry to the profession and strict control of professional behaviour under the auspices of the Royal College of Veterinary Surgeons.

In Chapter 3, Timothy Cox, Chairman of the Veterinary History Society, describes the early progress of veterinary practice in Newmarket and the difficulties experienced by colleagues who struggled to apply their art and science in the environs of the town, despite opposition from some of its multiple vested interests. The account reveals the many worthy individuals who actually practised in Newmarket, as far back as 1795; and the succession of practitioners over the next two centuries.

Alan Medlock, long-term member of the Jockey Club staff at Newmarket, contributes a history of the club in Chapter 4. The establishment of Newmarket as a world-renowned centre of horseracing was dependent upon the fact that the Jockey Club set up its meeting place here in the 18th century. It was from this early origin that the racehorse and Newmarket became internationally linked in terms of racing and breeding; and hence the *raison d'etre* for veterinary practice specialised to serve those requirements.

Chapters 5 and 6 provide an account of the first multi-member veterinary practice group to be established in Newmarket. Richard Greenwood, a senior partner in the practice that was started, by Livock and Reynolds in the early part of the last century, describes the development of that practice into its present form of the Newmarket Equine Hospital. Chapter 6 contains a tribute to the two mid-century doyens of the practice, Fred Day and Bob Crowhurst, by the highly respected and successful Newmarket trainer, Sir Mark Prescott.

Chapter 7 presents an account of a second practice which was started as a single-member endeavour in 1959 and has since grown over the years to a multi-member practice that established an equine hospital in nearby Exning in 1998. The contributors of the chapter are Sidney Ricketts and Nick Wingfield Digby, currently managing partners of the practice.

In Chapter 8, Peter Webbon describes the establishment of the Equine Research Station (ERS), at Balaton Lodge, Newmarket by the founder of the Animal Health Trust (AHT), Reginald Wooldridge in 1942. This expanded over the second half of the last century to occupy a site at Lanwades Park with research and referral facilities and a substantial number of staff. Chapter 8 includes memories of work at the ERS by such as Robert Cook, a pioneer in stable hygiene and associated respiratory ailments of horses, Leo Jeffcott recently retired as Dean of Sydney University Veterinary School and Tim Greet who joined the second practice in Newmarket and whose contribution to equine ENT medicine and surgery is well recognised.

Chapter 9 by Simon Curtis, a member of a distinguished family of farriers who have served the stud and stable inmates for two generations, discusses the place of farriery in the town. Simon's talents have been recognised by the Royal College of Veterinary Surgeons who bestowed an Honorary Associateship upon him.

Chapter 10 describes the history of the Equine Fertility Unit which was started in Cambridge in the seventies and moved to Mertoun Paddocks on the Woodditton Road, Newmarket, in the nineties. Its collaboration with the practices and other centres made a significant contribution to the understanding of reproductive biology of mares and stallions which has led directly and indirectly to improved fertility rates in practice. The very substantial endeavours of Professor W.R. (Twink) Allen in setting up and maintaining this valuable facility is highlighted.

From the Grassroots of Equine Practice

Background

As someone who has had the privilege of serving as a veterinarian in Newmarket for some 50 years, I have experience by which to form a judgement of the strengths and weaknesses of our profession in practice. I entered the profession in the 1950s because of a deep affinity with horses and riding. My teenage ambition was to become a jockey but my father and brothers, being in the medical profession, persuaded me in favour of following a medical or veterinary pathway.

Ensconced as a student on a small-holding at Brookland on the Romney Marsh, I had access to a few acres on which I reared and maintained a small number of sheep, pigs, a riding horse and a broodmare from whom I bred a foal which had the distinction of beating Gay Time in a nursery at Doncaster by a short-head. Mention of this is kindly made in Chapter 6. The horse was owned

in partnership with Albert Stafford-Smith of Cheveley Park Stud, Newmarket.

Peter Rossdale with foal in 1949, later named Pantomime Star and referred to in Chapter 6.

This partnership was formed when I gave a half share to Albert on learning of the untimely death of Nomellini who was the sire of the foal. It was through the friendship of Albert that I was destined to practice as a veterinarian in Newmarket.

Veterinary Education in the 1940's

At the Royal Veterinary College in my year, there were few students who had either the background for, or the desire to enter practice with the intention of specialising on horses. The exceptions were Richard (Dickie) Rees, of the family involved with racing, Jim Cunningham and Bill Walter. In contrast, John Ayliffe entered college with no experience of horses nor, indeed, of farm animals having been brought up in London before joining the army in the war. Nevertheless, he became a well-respected equine consultant in the practice at Ashford, Kent. There were those, such as Ian Silver, Bob Cook and Jack Payne who were clearly destined for scientific avenues as proved subsequently to be the case; and there were but 5 female students in a year of 75 compared with the 60-90% in the classes of today. There was little encouragement to question the validity of the orthodox views prevailing in veterinary medicine at that time.

Veterinary Services

My experience of equine practice has left me with impressions, opinions and, to a certain degree actual knowledge, of both the improving status and capabilities of the profession in the service of veterinary medicine and surgery and the welfare of horses. On the other side of the coin of service lie the interests of the owners and handlers of the horses affected by injury or disease.

Rowley mile grandstand viewed from heath grounds.

When I entered practice in the fifties there were few data as to the verification of diagnosis of conditions affecting horses and by which to monitor progress in cases under treatment. Haematological and blood biochemical values in health and disease were sparse. This was particularly evident with respect to foals in their first weeks of postnatal life, which encouraged me to collect such information on cases of sick newborn foals.

I became particularly involved with convulsing foals, known then as barkers due to the sounds they made during convulsion, and in premature or weak foals. In this I was encouraged by colleagues, especially Ian and Marian Silver, Lesley Hall and Tony Palmer at the Cambridge Veterinary School. My work on the barker foal was greatly assisted by the interest shown by Geoffrey Dawes and Geoffrey Thorburn of the Nuffield Medical Centre in Oxford who were internationally recognised experts in similar conditions in the human infant. They visited a

barker case at New England Stud one Sunday such was their comparative interest.

Leo Mahaffey, the pathologist at the ERS, impressed upon me the need to approach practice cases in the spirit of challenge, by questioning existing and untested avenues of diagnosis and treatments. My thesis in 1967 for a Fellowship of the Royal College of Veterinary Surgeons (FRCVS) entitled, *A clinical and laboratory assessment of the health status of the newborn foal,* was therefore based upon data obtained directly from sick and healthy foals, and subjected to statistical analysis. In retrospect, this was a somewhat precocious experience in what is currently regarded as evidence-based medicine (EBM), now much relied upon in medical and veterinary circles as essential to the proof of beneficial outcome of procedures of diagnosis and therapy.

Giving Service

The veterinary profession is committed to providing a service and the proof of progress is best summarised by comparing the positions of 50 years ago and those of today, in terms of the number of veterinarians engaged in equine practice and research.

In 1954, there were only some 10 colleagues involved. The Brayley Reynolds Practice (see Chapters 5 and 6) consisted of three partners, namely, Geoff Leader, Fred Day and Bob Crowhurst. Brayley Reynolds himself was retired but still resident in Newmarket and there were two assistants, namely Derek Grant and Shaun Collins. Charlie Townsend was responsible to a number of trainers but lived outside of Newmarket; and there were also those with commitments to stud farms and trainers who practised outside the Newmarket area, of which John Burkhart, in practice in Thirsk, Yorkshire, was the best known internationally.

The Animal Health Trust (AHT: see Chapter 8), at the time, was responsible for the Equine Research Station at Balaton Lodge. This was under the directorship of Professor William Miller. Its clinical referral centre was under the control of Jim Roberts (the surgeon who attended the fracture of Mill Reef), the haematologist Richard Archer who later became director of the station and Leo Mahaffey who had joined the station as a pathologist having been born and previously practised in Australia.

The AHT also had a small-animal unit at Kentford under the directorship of John Hodgson and a staff which included Brian Singleton, later to become the President of the Royal College of Veterinary Surgeons and Director of the Equine Research Station.

The Newmarket Clock Tower located at the top of the High Street. Local builder Richard Arber built it to commemorate Queen Victoria's golden jubilee of 1887. The clock tower was officially opened in 1890. Photo by courtesy Trevor Jones.

In 2010, there are over 100 veterinarians with livelihoods centred on the town. There are three practices comprising the employment and participation of some 60 veterinarians as partners, assistants, interns and residents.

Now, in the circumstances of this very substantial increase in the number of veterinarians, let us consider the reasons that lie behind this expansion. First on the list must be that of technology and, more particularly, of 'imaging' i.e. radiology, ultrasound, magnetic resonance imaging (MRI) and nuclear scintigraphy. The advances in the technology of surgery allied to improvements in anaesthetic techniques, together with those in medical therapies all contribute to the need for, and benefits of, increased veterinary personnel. Practice and AHT laboratories, with their highly qualified teams of veterinarians and technicians, make an essential contribution to improved means and accuracy of diagnosis.

Within the enormous range of technologies lies the need for specialists. Once, the vet in practice was expected to be an expert across the spectrum of clinical practice and to encompass the whole range of diagnostic approaches available at the time. This was indeed the basis for international reputations gained by individuals in practice, especially at certain centres such as Newmarket, Lexington, Yorkshire and Ireland.

Nowadays, the picture is quite different. Each colleague has a speciality either directly as a surgeon, an anaesthetist or imager, or in terms of the variety of case subjects and conditions related to such as foals, mares, stallions; and to lameness, infectious disease, reproductive performance or skin and specific organ problem, whether these be primarily related to the liver, nervous system, intestines etc.

Many specialities have developed from the background of generality in the context of clinicians having some knowledge across the range of cases met with in practice; but even the GP has his or her speciality with their range of caseload expertise. The veterinary practice performs its service as a whole and referrals often take place internally rather than, as in the medical health service, by GP diagnosis followed by referral to consultants and hospitals outside the practice.

It is the development of specialities based largely upon the substantial increase in the use of technology, that has required more vets to become established members of practices. These comprise a force that serves the equine industry and communities to a degree undreamt of fifty years ago.

This is particularly the case in places such as Newmarket where there is a large population of horses involved in Thoroughbred and non - Thoroughbred activities ranging from racing to three day eventing, endurance riding and other equine pursuits. The depth of expertise involved has stimulated the development of a substantial referral base for horses from other parts of the country.

Horses at exercise with St Agnes church in background. The church was built on behalf of Caroline Agnes, Duchess of Montrose, a member of the Episcopal Church of Scotland, in memory of her second husband, W. S. Stirling Crawfurd. His body was interred in a plot behind the church in 1885. On October 8th, 1887, it was consecrated by the Bishop of Ely. When the duchess died in 1894 she was buried beside her husband in the plot behind the church, marked by a standing cross.

The Animal Health Trust has based its activities in this country in both treatment of clinical referral cases and research into various aspects of equine diseases. Peter Webbon, the one time veterinary advisor to the Jockey Club and now director of AHT, has a distinguished staff of clinicians lead by Sue Dyson, and a team of researchers described in Chapters 8. The influence of the width and depth of their expertise has expanded clinical practice both in Newmarket and within the veterinary profession generally.

Top of their pops:Three Newmarket trainers seen on Warren Hill gallop, each having trained Epsom Derby winners, namely Sir Michael Stoute (n=5: Shergar, Shahrastani, Kris Kin, North Light and Workforce), Sir Henry Cecil (n=4: Slip Anchor, Reference Point, Commander in Chief and Oath) and Michael Bell (n=1: Motivator). Michael Holding is on foot. He was born 16 February 1954 in Kingston, Jamaica. One of the fastest bowlers ever to play Test cricket, and nicknamed 'Whispering Death' by umpires due to his quiet approach to the bowling crease. Photo courtesy Trevor Jones, Thoroughbredphoto Ltd (2005).

The Cambridge University Veterinary School is within 14 miles of Newmarket and its staff of clinical and research experts provide integrated and close interaction with members of the staff, clinicians and research workers in Newmarket as described by Peter Jackson in Chapter 2. The school was started in 1949 and its graduates have served equine practices in Newmarket while at the same time the practices have contributed to undergraduate education through the custom of enabling students to "see practice" as part of their training.

Receiving Service

The question should now be asked as to what the services available have contributed to the benefit of horses and their owners and handlers over the years; and the extent to which these benefits have improved over that time.

Built in 1903, the Rothschild Yard at Palace House Stables, as it is today after restoration work.

a). Equine welfare: The veterinary ethos has always been, as with doctors, when presented with a case to follow the Hippocratic oath, to do no harm and to care for the welfare of the patient. In equine practice, development towards these objectives has paralleled the advancement in technology and drug therapy; in association with new knowledge regarding pain and how to control it.

Colic cases are an example that illustrate the changes in practice that occurred from the fifties to the present decade. In the fifties the means of diagnosis were very limited with respect to identifying the cause of colic in particular cases. These range from simple spasmodic (wind) to volvulus (twist). Remedies were similarly restricted to pethidine/morphine compounds injected and to liquid paraffin and anti-spasmolyitics administered via a stomach tube. Consequently cases either recovered or died after prolonged periods of acute pain.

Nowadays diagnosis of cause is much more accurate through the use of aids such as imaging and laboratory tests. Powerful pain-relieving drugs are available and surgery is a highly effective route to cure of obstructions such as twisted gut.

b). Owner interests: Probably the most important aspect from which owners benefit from veterinary service is in the means and accuracy of diagnosis. It is, after all, upon the diagnosis of the condition/illness/disease that prognosis (probable outcome) of the case depends; and on which the appropriate treatment must be based.

In the fifties, diagnosis was largely intuitive whereas today it is much more scientific; and monitored together with therapy applied, by critical review which constitutes EBM (Evidence-based medicine).

The importance to the owners of horses of accurate diagnosis cannot be over-emphasised, for it is through accurate diagnosis that we assess therapeutic needs, potential outcome and financial consequences of such conditions as lameness, reproductive inefficiency, poor performance and any long-term consequences that may interfere at some later stage in the animal's life, whether for racing, hunting, jumping or riding for pleasure.

c). Examples of benefits of modern: veterinary service: Scintigraphy allows the identification of stress fractures long before they become catastrophic. This provides the opportunity to avoid such a disastrous outcome.

d). Challenges of veterinary practice: Costs, genetic inheritance and welfare issues are those that require continuing dialogue between vets, owners, horse handlers and the general public. Suffice here to say that many attitudes are dependent upon vested interests and some, perhaps even those held by the same individual or organisation, are mutually incompatible.

The vet's aim is to be professional (objective) at all times and to provide a service 24 hours/day for 365 days of the year. This service is equivalent to the general practice of doctors and hospital availability of the National Health Service (NHS) combined, which is inevitably a costly enterprise with associated overheads.

Owners rightly expect accurate diagnoses, effective treatments and preventive measures. This comes at a cost and the economic balance between effort and outcome is understandably important to owners and vets alike.

The greater the veterinary benefits of restoring function to injured and diseased horses, the more we have to consider the extent to which these deficits are based on the genetics of the individual concerned. This is of greatest concern in connection with the breeding of horses that are sound for the purpose of their usage.

The welfare of the horse is of concern to all of us, vets, owners and general public. The need for research into better methods of diagnosis and treatment outcome has been, and will always be, the central issue with regard to progress. Fifty years ago the opinions of experts were those upon which we all depended. Nowadays the challenge is for evidence to support opinion. This is called evidence-based medicine (EBM) and all decisions in practice and those taken by owners, trainers etc should follow this demanding avenue.

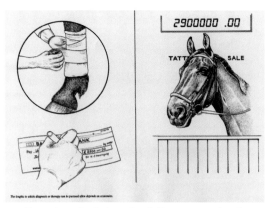

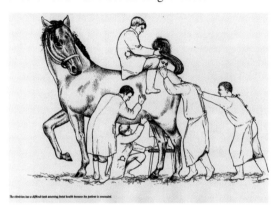

Illustrating the hands on approach to diagnosis before imaging techniques were available (Ultrasound, endoscopy, MRI). Drawing by John Fuller.

Horses are impatient patients. John Fuller.

Drawing depicting the delicate strands of veterinary service; namely, type of injury, value of individual and the costs of therapy with probability of outcome. John Fuller.

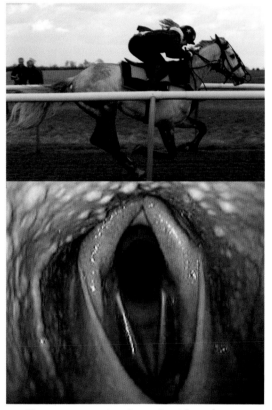

Horse at exercise (upper) with endoscope in place providing view of vocal chords in action (lower). Courtesy Gregory Sommerville BVSc MRCVS.

Examples of the modern art and science of equine practice
courtesy of Sarah Powell VetMB MRCVS

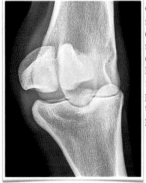 Computed radiography image (2D) of the right metcarpophalangeal (fetlock) joint of a horse with fragmentation of the palmar process of the proximal phalanx (P1).

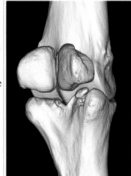 Computed radiography image of the same fetlock joint. The two dimensional data set has been reconstructed into a 3D image.

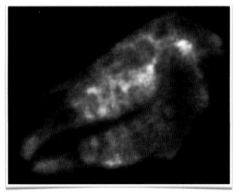

Bone phase scintigraphy (bone scan) image of the equine head. Scintigraphy has traditionally been used to assess the equine dental arcades for the presence of sinonasal disease.

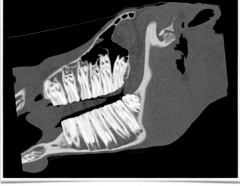

Multiplanar reformatted computed tomographic image of the equine dental arcades. CT has afforded the modern equine clinician infinite detail of the dental arcades and sinuses.

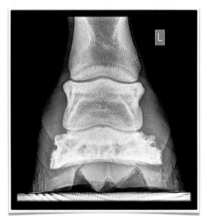

Dorsopalmar computed tomographic projection of the equine foot.

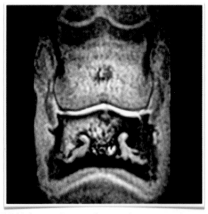

Multiplanar reformatted magnetic resonance image of the same foot acquired under standing sedation. A midline osseous cyst-like lesion is present in the pedal bone, as is a lateral wing fracture

Chapter 2

Veterinary Education with Special References to Equine Studies

by: Peter Jackson MA FRCVS

*P*eter Jackson qualified from Edinburgh in 1960 and spent the next 16 years in general practice at March. Cambs. He was appointed as Lecturer in Veterinary Obstetrics at Edinburgh in 1976. He came back to his hometown of Cambridge in 1980 when appointed to the post of University Physician at Cambridge Veterinary School a post he held until he took early retirement in 1999. He continued to teach part time until 2006 and was appointed Senior Tutor at St Edmund's College Cambridge from 2002 until 2006. He has been a trustee at Wood Green Animal Shelters since 2002.

Early Days and the London College

Formal veterinary education in the UK began with the opening in 1791 of the London Veterinary College. This was sometimes referred to as the St Pancras Veterinary College indicating its location in the capital. Over the past 219 years, there has been, in general terms, a steady improvement in the quality of teaching and the knowledge of the profession. There have been setbacks in veterinary education in both the UK and in other countries often associated with financial constraints and a lack of good teaching staff.

The excitement, which accompanied the opening at London, was short lived. Professor Charles St Bel, who had been appointed to head the college, died suddenly in 1793 - possibly of glanders (Bacterial disease of horses). The college was in danger of closing and there were very few trained UK veterinarians to take the place of St Bel.

William Moorcroft an Englishman who had studied veterinary medicine in France was a possible successor to St Bel but was unwilling to leave his London practice. Edward Coleman a human surgeon aged 28 was appointed to lead the college and Moorcroft agreed to help out when possible. Coleman admitted that he was *'little versed in veterinary matters and was presumptuous to superintend the interests and growth of the infant profession.'*

Coleman remained in post for the next 40 years and although he was said to have *'an acute and active mind'* he showed minimal empathy to his animal patients. He survived a number of attempts to remove him from office but it wasn't until The Veterinarian was published in 1828 that criticism of Coleman and his college could be co-ordinated.

The London College styled itself *'The Royal Veterinary College'* in 1826 through receiving the patronage of King George IV. However an editorial in The Veterinarian in 1830 noted that the late King was 'becoming much displeased by the late management of that institution. In 1875 the 'Royal' title of the London College was consolidated when Queen Victoria granted it a charter of incorporation.

St Bel had planned a three - year course at London but Coleman abandoned this programme and students were presented for examination after spending a very few months at the college. Students were not required to provide evidence of a good education before coming to college. Most of the examiners for the London College's diploma were medically qualified and none held a veterinary qualification. It was suggested that such persons as the examiners were unlikely to have any knowledge about diseases of the horse and how they might be treated.

The problems experienced by veterinary surgeons trying to establish a practice at Newmarket in 1831 have been alluded to in one chapter. Given the poor state of veterinary education in the UK at that time it is perhaps not surprising that veterinary surgeons were held in such poor regard.

Writing in the Veterinarian, a veterinary surgeon who styled himself 'WJG' was of the opinion that 'The student leaves St Pancras just as ignorant as the professors themselves. It is the want of such knowledge that makes the veterinary surgeon appear more ignorant than he really is. The same author said *'It is then not to be so much wondered at when the gentlemen of Newmarket prefer the knowledge of their groom to that of a tinker particularly when the groom has been accustomed from his boyhood to the care of horses'*.

H.M. The Queen signing the visitors book when she opened Cambridge Veterinary School in October1955.

In 1844, an important milestone in the veterinary profession's history was reached when The Royal College of Veterinary Surgeons (RCVS) was granted a Royal Charter and became a body corporate responsible for the early regulation of veterinary education. The RCVS arranged examinations for their Membership Diploma and students awarded the diploma were recognised as qualified veterinary surgeons.

Other UK Veterinary Schools

William Dick's Veterinary College had been established at Clyde Street in Edinburgh in 1823 and its students were initially examined and certified by the Highland & Agricultural Society of Scotland. In 1844, the first examinations for the MRCVS diploma were held by the RCVS in Edinburgh.

Edinburgh might have appeared to be well supplied with veterinary colleges and at some periods of history the city had two veterinary colleges. John Gamgee opened the first New Edinburgh College in 1857 but transferred it to London where it became the Albert School in 1867. In 1874 William Williams who had briefly been principal of the Dick College opened a

second New Edinburgh College. This was transferred to Liverpool and was attached to the University in 1904.

Glasgow Veterinary College was established in 1862 and became affiliated to Glasgow University in 1949 as a result of the 1949 Veterinary Surgeons Act. The Veterinary College of Ireland was established in 1900 and the veterinary schools at Bristol and Cambridge were established in 1949.

Cambridge already had an Institute of Animal Pathology, which had been set up in 1923, and the Medical Research Council had endowed a Professorship of Animal Pathology there. In 1949 the Institute of Pathology became a Department of Animal Pathology and joined with a new Department of Veterinary Clinical Studies to form the Veterinary School at Madingley Road, Cambridge. A School of Veterinary Medicine & Science was established at Nottingham University in 2005.

Over the years the RCVS increased the length of their Membership course and their programme of examinations was refined. In 1876 a three - year course was established with both oral and practical examinations. A certificate of general education was an entry requirement of the course from 1888 and in 1892 a written examination was added to the oral and practical examinations. In 1895 the course was extended to four years and a further extension to five years was instituted in 1932.

When the Veterinary Surgeons Act of 1881 was passed only persons holding the MRCVS Diploma could call themselves veterinary surgeons. A few years previously in 1876 Robert Koch had discovered the cause of anthrax to be a bacterium and other discoveries regarding the infectious cause of disease rapidly followed.

The Animal Health Trust (AHT) was established in 1943 as the Veterinary Education Trust and has played a major part in research and in clinical work (see Chapter 8). Originally it had farm animal, small animal and equine sections. The Equine Research Station was based at Snailwell Road in Newmarket but later moved to share Landwades Park with the small animal section of the AHT.

Unrecognisable Changes

In the last century the veterinary profession has undergone almost unimaginable changes and these have been most noticeable during the last fifty years. There is now much more openness within the profession with a healthy tendency to share new knowledge and techniques. Fifty years ago there was an atmosphere of secrecy between practices and relatively little contact with veterinary schools even within the same county. At that time veterinary surgeons were not allowed to advertise their services and specialists were not formally recognised within the profession.

Most practices were 'mixed' and were expected to deal with all the domestic species and newly qualified veterinary surgeons were expected to be omni-competent. The practices were often located in small towns and provided service to farm animals and horses in the towns and surrounding villages. Most also ran a clinic for small animal cases once or twice daily.

University Connection

Since the 1949 Veterinary Surgeons Act all the UK's veterinary colleges have become integral parts of their local university. All students now work for a bachelor of veterinary medicine and surgery degree leading to admission to the RCVS membership diploma allowing them to practice as veterinary surgeons. An RCVS inspection and approval of each veterinary school is held at regular intervals and is carried out to ensure that standards remain high at each school. A EU inspection of each school also takes place.

The research record of each veterinary school and its university are also examined under the Research Assessment Exercise (RAE). Initially this was carried out through a detailed inspection by a team of examiners but recently a degree of self-assessment has been allowed. Each school hopes to gain the maximum grade of 5 since this will have an effect on the level of research funding and also identify centres of excellence.

There is healthy competition between the UK's veterinary schools and some welcome rivalry too. Veterinarians in academia are expected to publish the results of their research work and to discuss new clinical techniques. There is now a free exchange of views and willingness for colleagues to learn from each other on a world - wide basis.

The Association of Veterinary Students (AVS) represents students from all the UK veterinary schools and also students from the Republic of Ireland. Annual conferences are organized at each of the veterinary schools in turn where social activities including sports are enjoyed along with clinical papers and practical demonstrations.

The Curriculum

Veterinary knowledge is increasing at an exponential rate and the schools make every effort to ensure that new graduates leave their alma mater with the most up to date knowledge possible. In the UK students are still expected to show a degree of omni-competence and to leave their veterinary school with the ability to demonstrate Day One Competences (see also below).

Traditionally, veterinary tuition followed a fixed pattern. Students were required to enter veterinary school with a good knowledge of the basic sciences or to gain such knowledge before they began the veterinary course proper. Preclinical studies followed in which anatomy, physiology, biochemistry and animal husbandry including animal handling were taught. The paraclinical course followed in which pharmacology and the causes of disease were taught. Subject matter included Pathology, Microbiology and Parasitology.

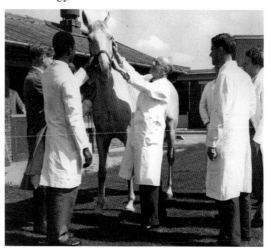

Professor LP Pugh, Professor of Veterinary Clinical Studies, demonstrating the examination of a horse to a group of Clinical Students at Cambridge during the 1950s.

The final two years of the course were the Clinical years in which the student was at last allowed to see living animals and attend classes in Medicine, Surgery and Obstetrics including infertility. Each subject was allocated quite a large number of lectures and these were often not well illustrated and notes had to be taken at speed. Photocopying of handouts and word processing was not available.

Much of the clinical teaching took place with quite large groups of students being taught together. Ten or more students might be invited to look at a single dog, cow or horse in the clinic. One student would be chosen to take the patient's temperature whilst another took the pulse and another looked at the colour of the mucus membranes. Each clinical department had relatively few clinicians and thus large group teaching was inevitable although not particularly effective.

Some techniques such as rectal examination of the mare - which is so important in stud practice - were not taught because of the perceived danger to students or to the mares they were examining. There was little contact with owners except at the first opinion free small animal clinics that most schools ran and which were attended by final year students. If students were very lucky they might be allowed to spay a single cat during a surgery practical or to share the operation with another student.

Lame horses were reasonably plentiful in most veterinary schools because horse - drawn vehicles were still quite heavily used for bread and milk delivery. Many of the veterinary schools had their own farm where farm animals could be examined and some ran a large animal practice at which groups of students could see farm animal and equine cases.

Textbooks, Journals and Visual Aids

The veterinary student of today is extremely well supplied with a wide range of textbooks. For the most part they are of the highest quality and well illustrated by colour photographs. In the equine field some cover broad topics such as medicine or surgery whilst others are more specialised and deal in greater detail with topics such as colic, lameness and endoscopy. The only limit to what students may purchase is the depth of their pocket. Many of the books are available as printed versions and are also available in electronic format. Fifty years ago students had a poor selection of books and many were out of date as the result of restrictions in printing during the Second World War.

A wide variety of national and international journals are available to the modern student. The Equine Veterinary Journal (EVJ) was among the first journals devoted to the horse and was originally set up and published by the British Equine Veterinary Association (BEVA). An offshoot of the EVJ has been the Equine Journal of Education in which review articles of specific topics such as equine choke are aimed chiefly at the veterinary student. Some journals are available in electronic format and some are offered to students at a discounted price.

Visual aids to teaching have also improved greatly. Coloured photographic slides replaced black and white photos but they in turn have been superseded by Microsoft PowerPoint presentations to illustrate lectures or as stand-alone teaching aids. Students also use interactive aids to illustrate techniques, cover topics of interest or as self - assessments. As a further aid to learning students are also asked to prepare short presentations for their colleagues and staff on topics of interest.

Early Introduction to Clinical Work

Now in many of the veterinary schools students meet and handle living animals and see clinical cases in the first few weeks of their course. Anatomy is taught by dissection supplemented by a study of surface anatomy on living animals and also with an introduction to radiographic and ultrasonographic anatomy.

Lectures still form an important part of most courses but frantic note taking is avoided by lecturers supplying comprehensive handouts covering the main points in any lecture. At the new veterinary school at Nottingham a 'paper - free' culture prevails. Students are provided with a lap top computer when they join the first year of the course and are able to download lecture notes and other materials. Most examinations are also taken on line.

Intercalated Degrees

These are available at some schools and allow the student to take a year out from the veterinary course and study in a preclinical or paraclinical area before returning to the main veterinary curriculum. A popular subject is veterinary pathology and the successful student is awarded a BSc on completion of the course.

At Cambridge the majority of students undertake a special period of study during the third year of the six - year veterinary course. Cambridge students take the Medical & Veterinary Sciences Tripos, which covers the first three years of their course, and are awarded a BA degree once this is successfully completed. The third year of the tripos allows a period in which a subject with veterinary connections can be studied in depth and the student is expected to undertake some research. At the end of the year students submit a dissertation and it is hoped that some may be encouraged to follow a research career at a later date. Affiliated Cambridge students who already hold a good science degree are excused the third tripos year and can complete their veterinary degree in five years instead of six.

The Lecture - Free Final Year and Clinical Rotations

This excellent development is now found in all the UK veterinary schools. The entire final year is spent on clinical rotations in which groups of four or five students are assigned to a clinical subject and during the year students visit each rotation. At Cambridge for example students spend four weeks on the Equine Rotation and are involved with cases both in the equine hospital and on the ambulatory clinic. They will be involved in all aspects of case management from the admission of patients, assisting with surgery in theatre and are heavily involved in nursing care.

The exposure to clinical material is much greater under this system of teaching. Students are now much better prepared for going into practice or for further study. At the end of each rotation the performance of each student is assessed. Any student who has not performed satisfactorily may be required to repeat and pass that rotation during the vacation.

Removing all lectures from the final year timetable has meant that all the lecture courses in the clinical course have been drastically reduced. Covering the ever - increasing amount of knowledge for each subject in a shorter period of time has presented great challenges. Despite this the lecture free final year has been so successful that it is likely to remain an essential part of veterinary training.

The additional small group clinical teaching in the lecture free final year has necessitated the appointment of more clinical staff. Much of the funding of this has come from hospital income and the additional case - load required. Comparison of the number of veterinary staff in the schools in 1960 and 2010 has shown that for example staffing levels have increased by 400% at the Royal Veterinary College and by 270% at Cambridge Veterinary School.

Final Year Electives

After completion of all the final year rotations, each student is required to choose a further short period of elective study. Students wishing to work with horses will probably hope to join the Equine Elective if space is available. During the elective students work with case material and also attend a number of seminars given either by school staff or outside lecturers.

Each student also undertakes a short research project during their elective with work being carried out for this either within the school's hospital or outside. Students are examined on their elective performance and must pass this along with their final examinations before being allowed to graduate. In some cases students have been able to publish their research work in refereed journals.

Extra Mural Study (EMS)

Formerly known as 'seeing practice' EMS has been compulsory for veterinary undergraduates for many years. Prior to the 1949 Veterinary Surgeons Act students could undertake locums and gain personal experience in this way. Most arranged to see practice at a local veterinary surgery. Additional funding was not available and it was less expensive to live at home whilst gaining the necessary 26 weeks practice experience. As most practices were really mixed it was possible to complete the whole 26 weeks requirement at the local vets. Cases of all species could be seen including the statutory six cases of 'parturition in the larger farm animals.' Some practices insisted that students committed themselves to do their whole 26 weeks of EMS with them expecting that they would become really helpful to the practice as they went through their course.

The veterinary schools realised how variable

the quality of EMS might be and insisted that students experienced some mixed practice in addition to more specialized small animal, equine and farm animal practice. Some experience could be obtained in the schools' own practices during the vacation. Some schools allotted each of their students to a Clinical Adviser who helped them plan their EMS and looked at reports received from practices after the students left. In some schools lists of 'good practices for EMS' are preserved and in others practices are signed up to become 'foster practices' taking chiefly or only students from that school.

Specialist practices have become much sought after as places at which students could see for example equine practice. The two larger Newmarket practices have waiting lists for students who wish to spend time with them and many students book their time up a year or so in advance.

Students who are able to afford it may plan to see practice abroad and this may include visits to some of the leading equine clinics in the USA or Europe. Such overseas opportunities are much sought after and gaining access to them is highly competitive. Finding placements for meat inspection or with the Veterinary Laboratory Agency can be difficult particularly since the number of veterinary undergraduates has increased.

The Final Examinations

At the end of their five or six year period of study students must sit their final examinations. Theoretically they can legitimately be asked questions on any topic from the whole of the undergraduate course. In fact the final examinations concentrate chiefly on the Clinical Subjects. Four written papers cover Small Animals, Farm Animals, Equine Studies and Animal Health respectively.

At one time in addition to their written papers students had to complete a clinical examination in each area but this work is now examined during clinical rotations. Oral examinations are held in each subject and students are assessed as to whether they have passed or failed each subject and also whether they have reached either a merit or distinction standard. External examiners from other veterinary schools aided by local staff conduct examinations.

Clinicians from the equine practices in Newmarket have been involved as external examiners and some hold honorary lectureships or professorial chairs at a number of veterinary schools. Such people often also help by giving lectures and having groups of students at their clinics to see cases of interest. This has been of great help to the Cambridge school when there has been at times an 'inter - regnum' before a new member of staff is appointed following a retirement.

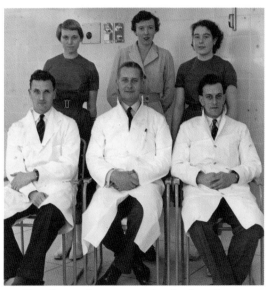

The Surgical team at Cambridge Veterinary School in 1954.
Back row (l to r) Miss P Pegram, Miss M White, Miss MA Fletcher
Front row (l to r) Mr RG Walker, Col J Hickman, Dr LW Hall.

The Professional Development Phase (PDP)

Since 2007 UK veterinary graduates have been required to register for this post - qualification period of additional training in practice. A senior colleague in the practice is appointed to supervise the new member and be ready to help with any aspects of career development and clinical competence. The aim of the PDP phase is to provide a structure whereby new graduates can continue to develop their professional and clinical skills, reflect on their progress and plan their professional development. The PDP system is also useful for veterinary surgeons who are returning to work after career breaks or are moving to a different area of work such as small animal to equine practice.

The RCVS has developed a web - based database in which new graduates can log their experience across a range of clinical skills and procedures in Small Animal, Equine or Farm Animal Practice. The graduate is expected to develop 'Year 1' skills during their PDP phase.

Every new graduate is allocated an RCVS - appointed postgraduate dean who will be available online to provide guidance on completion of the records and who will review clinical logs before the graduate is confirmed as having completed their PDP. In some ways this may be seen as another layer of bureaucracy to be dealt with before the graduate is recognised as being fully prepared for practice. On the other hand stories are still heard about new graduates left to fend for themselves with minimal support being grudgingly given.

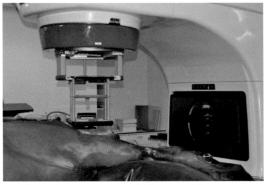

An eighteen - year - old horse with a meningioma undergoing radiation therapy at Cambridge Veterinary School.

Postgraduate Study and Qualifications

As in other professions, the basic veterinary qualification is now regarded as a professional starting point rather than a licence to practice for the indefinite future. RCVS Members are now required to undertake at least 35 hours of postgraduate study each year and to keep a record of the work they have done.

Although membership of the Royal College of Veterinary Surgeons entitles a graduate to work within the profession many vets go on to seek further qualifications. Postgraduate clinical qualifications have proliferated over the last 50

years. The Royal College of Veterinary Surgeons was the main provider of such qualifications in the UK.

Initially two diplomas were awarded - the Diploma in Veterinary Anaesthesia and the Diploma in Radiology. A range of species based qualifications followed at Certificate level - aimed at those working in practice and at Diploma level - where candidates were recommended to work in a university department or specialist clinic.

Examples in equine subjects include the Certificate in Equine Orthopaedics (Cert EO) and the Diploma in Equine Stud Medicine (DESM). These qualifications were challenging to candidates and were highly regarded. In recent years - perhaps controversially - many of these RCVS qualifications have been withdrawn and candidates now work for qualifications awarded by a number of European Colleges. In the horse an example is the Diploma of the European College of Equine Internal Medicine (DipECIM).

Since 2007 the RCVS has offered a series of modular certificates in Advanced Veterinary Practice. Although many regret the demise of the original RCVS certificates and diplomas the new certificates are claimed to offer a more flexible approach to veterinary postgraduate qualifications. The veterinary schools and other universities now teach some of the modular courses. A number of private companies also provide postgraduate veterinary courses.

The PhD and Higher Professional Degrees

The degree of doctor of philosophy (PhD) is awarded for a successful thesis written after a period of full time research usually completed over three years. The degree is now regarded as an essential qualification for those contemplating an academic career - even one in a clinical discipline. The research is usually laboratory based but may have a clinical connection.

The need for this degree presents the young veterinary surgeon with a number of problems. The first of these is finding funding for duration of the degree and a university department in which to carry out the required research. Another perceived but major problem is the need to take time out from clinical training to complete the PhD. Postgraduate students often agonise about whether to complete their PhD immediately after qualification or to delay working for their PhD until they have obtained a postgraduate clinical qualification.

In some universities the PhD can be taken part - time over a period of about seven years whilst the student continues with clinical work. Older clinicians with an extensive list of publications may be awarded a PhD through meritorious contribution to science. In recent years many veterinary schools have established Higher Professional Doctorates such as the VetMD at Cambridge and the DVM&S at Edinburgh. These degrees are also research based but may, unlike the PhD, be completed by those who are engaged in full time clinical work.

The Fellowship of the RCVS can be gained by research and the production of a thesis and provides another prestigious route by which to gain postgraduate qualifications.

The British Veterinary Association (BVA)

Sometimes described as the veterinary surgeons' trade union the BVA has over 12,000 members. It has 30 territorial and 21 specialist divisions. The territorial divisions represent members in various parts of the UK and also provide reasonably priced postgraduate study for their members. The specialist divisions are much younger than the territorial divisions and in some ways recognize the profession's need for specialist study.

The British Equine Veterinary Association (BEVA) is an important specialist division. The BEVA founded its own association journal the Equine Veterinary Journal and also the Journal of Equine Veterinary Education. BEVA holds an annual congress to which it attracts equine specialists from a worldwide audience to hear papers on the very latest equine veterinary topics and demonstrations of the latest techniques.

Specialisation in the Veterinary Profession

For many years the RCVS was unwilling to recognise the need for specialisation within the profession perhaps still wishing to believe that its members could be omnicompetent. The fact that some practices were already confining their work to a single species such as the horse and that members had recognized the need for the specialist BVA divisions, brought specialisation nearer.

Indeed the RCVS itself was providing

postgraduate qualifications and finally agreed to publish a list of RCVS Registered Specialists to promote specialization within the profession. The list would enable veterinary surgeons and the public to identify RCVS members who had specialist knowledge and skills and who were active practitioners of their speciality. Specialists would accept patient referrals from other veterinary surgeons and would maintain their specialist knowledge by continuing professional development.

The RCVS agreed that those on their specialist lists would normally possess an RCVS diploma or similar postgraduate qualification and would be acknowledged by their peers in the area of their speciality. Specialists would maintain their own professional development by publishing their work, speaking at national and international meetings and examining. They would be willing to receive referral cases and be active within their field.

In the List of Specialists in the Veterinary Register of 2010 13 members were listed as being specialists in Equine Medicine and 29 as specialists in Equine Surgery.

Postscript

Major advances in veterinary knowledge have taken place in the past 219 years and perhaps especially in the past 50 years. The structure and function of the horse are now known down to molecular and genetic levels. Other chapters in this book describe some of the new diagnostic techniques that are now available to the equine practitioner. The clinician, presented with a case may still say '*It looks like a case of ragwort poisoning and I don't think the outlook for recovery is good.*' The certainty of the diagnosis can be confirmed by further investigation.

The patient can now be effectively and expertly examined and its case history including possible access to the alkaloids of the poisonous plant, carefully assessed. The horse may show weight loss, dropsy and possibly the ominous abnormal behavioural signs of hepatic encephalopathy. A good methodical clinical examination remains of paramount importance and the temptation to use clinical pathology as a diagnosis in itself rather than as an aid to diagnosis must be resisted.

A blood sample will enable the clinician to detect abnormalities in the blood including a prolonged prothrombin time which may be attributed to liver damage. The red blood cells may be haemolysed leading to jaundice and anaemia. Biochemical studies on the blood will show low protein levels and raised liver enzymes suggesting the liver is damaged. An ultrasonographic scan may reveal evidence of hepatic cirrhosis.

A liver biopsy can be readily taken to confirm the presence of liver pathology although a low prothrombin time may indicate poor clotting ability of the blood. Care must be taken to avoid a haemorrhage when taking the biopsy. The degree of liver damage can be estimated and will help confirm the poor prognosis of this unpleasant condition. Humane euthanasia may be required. The laboratory tests and special diagnostic techniques will add greatly to the cost of the case but do much to confirm the diagnosis and add weight to the assessment of prognosis.

References
1. Anon (1830) The Veterinarian. 3 420.
2. Anon (1831) The Veterinarian 4 455 - 462.
3. Anon (1960) The Register of Veterinary Surgeons. Historical notes London. Royal College of Veterinary Surgeons. 531 - 534.

Further Reading
Pattison I (1984) The British Veterinary Profession 1791 - 1948. London.
JA Allen & Company Ltd.,

Acknowledgements
Grateful thanks for their help with the illustrations to Lorraine Leonard, Avice O' Connor, Alison Schwabe and Katie Snalune all of Cambridge Veterinary School.

Cambridge Equine Elective Students learning horse rescue techniques with clinical staff and members of the Hampshire Fire and Rescue Service.

Fire brigade in action in practice rescuing horse from swimming pool with Michael Hunt in veterinary charge.

Lord Soulsby of Swaffham Prior. Lawson was dean of the Cambridge Veterinary School 1978-1993. He is the first and only veterinary Life Peer.

Rotunda hospital building 1954

Chapter 3

For the Want of a Veterinarian

by: Timothy Cox MA

T im Cox spent thirty-six years in the media departments of London advertising agencies retiring as the world-wide media director on the Gillette account and the European media director for BBDO. He is a geography graduate of Cambridge University. Since retirement he has spent his time to building up a library devoted to all aspects of the thoroughbred horse. He is currently Chairman of the Veterinary History Society, a Trustee of the National Horseracing Museum and the Home of Horseracing Trust and the former Chairman of the Executive Committee of the British Sporting Art Trust.

A Poisonous Episode

On Wednesday 1st May 1811 six horses drank from a trough on Newmarket Heath. At that time trainers had their own drinking-troughs on the Heath near to the Well Gap in the Devil's Dyke. The troughs were kept covered and padlocked. The lids were made to fit tightly but they did buckle when left out in the sun. All six horses were in good health but all refused their corn when they returned to the stable. The well had been poisoned by injecting arsenic through a tube inserted under the lid. Subsequently four horses died. Richard Prince trained all six horses. Sir Sitwell Sitwell owned the two horses that survived; Sir Frank Standish and Lord Foley owned those that died.

John Kent, Richard Prince's head lad, acted promptly. He administered a strong dose of castor oil to Sir Sitwell's horses, Reveller and Coelebs[1]. Both horses recovered and ran in many races with Coelebs winning seven races in the following year. Weatherbys reported that vinegar had been applied to Sir Sitwell's horses and published a notice in their Annual Calendar suggesting that vinegar was a strong antidote to arsenic poisoning, something that *'appeared to us too important not to be mentioned, especially as it is not generally known even amongst medical men'*[2]. John Kent's son, also John Kent, took strong exception to this notice on behalf of his father.

The other horses had to wait for the arrival of Dr. Bowles of Cambridge, *'who was a certified physician for human beings, and also very clever in treating quadrupeds'*[3]. The delay in treating the

horses proved fatal. Spaniard, The Dandy, Pirouette and Sir Frank Standish's Colt by Eagle died in great agony. Kent reported that *'he had never seen a poor animal endure anything like the sufferings sustained by Spaniard, before death brought him merciful relief'*[4].

Cecil Bishop, a retired pharmacist, who was working on behalf of Daniel Dawson had put the arsenic in the well. Dawson, in turn, was working as a tout for two bookmakers, the brothers Joe and Jim Bland[5]. Prince's stable had a reputation as a gambling stable and his horses had been heavily backed in the ante-post market for the Newmarket First Spring Meeting. The Blands could not afford for them to win. The intention had been to incapacitate the horses, not kill them. But Prince had heard rumours about the wells being tampered with and had avoided using them for seventeen days before the fateful day[6]. The conspirators thought the arsenic was not working because the horses looked so well and therefore added more arsenic to the water. Eventually Dawson was caught, Bishop *'made a voluntary and written confession of the whole of the nefarious conspiracy'*, and Dawson was found guilty and sentenced to be hanged. As an aside, Dawson was acquitted at his first trial on a legal point and had to be retried on a different set of charges[7].

This tale contains many of the elements of the early history of the veterinary profession in Newmarket. John Kent, junior considered *'the veterinary art to be at a low ebb at this time'*. However, he described his father as *'a capital 'vet'*, although all his knowledge had been acquired by rule of thumb'*[8]. Even Weatherbys were prepared to peddle unsubstantiated cures for arsenic poisoning in the 'official' record of the sport, based on rumour and gossip.

John Bowles

Charles Vial de Saint Bel set up the Royal Veterinary College (RVC) in 1791. John Bowles was one of its early graduates. He enrolled in 1798 and qualified in December of that year at the age of 33 years. Although he was described as *'a certified physician for human beings'* and as *'Dr Bowles of Cambridge',* a detailed search by the Royal Society of Medicine Library Services has found no evidence that he passed any medical exams. But, if he was not a qualified physician what was he doing up to the age of 33? He set up in business in Regent's Street, Cambridge as a veterinary surgeon and shoeing smith - a shoeing forge was a necessary part of a successful equine practice in those days. Although he arrived too late to save the poisoned horses, he did carry out the autopsy on them. The Veterinarian magazine described him as *'a very excellent practitioner'*[9]. When he died in 1834, his obituary in the Sporting Magazine[10] said:

'On 12th January Veterinary Science lost one of its brightest ornaments and its best advocates...known by the great, for honor, honesty, and uprightness in all his dealings, and ... his extraordinary skill ...: by the middle ranks, for his affability, ... kindness, humanity and assiduity when administering to their afflicted and suffering animals, ... ever anxious to bring about the greatest possible cure at the least possible expense: [and] by the poor, ... generously charitable, with as much anxiety to relieve from pain and restore to health and soundness the poor man's donkey as the Prince's race-horse; .. '.

Mr. Bowles[11] was one of the first members of his profession to treat diseases of horses in a scientific manner, as opposed to the rule-of-thumb methods of old-fashioned practitioners. Having speedily acquired a reputation in the University and town, his fame spread through Cambridgeshire and the adjoining counties; and Newmarket was among the first places to avail itself of his skill. During a long period of practice, he treated nearly every horse of note trained at headquarters, carefully adapting his treatment to the circumstances of the case. When called in to find out the ailment of a racehorse, he gave unusual

time and care to the performance of his duty. Having settled the question of what was the matter, he would invariably ask what engagements the animal had. *'If he has three engagements in April, where is the use,'* Mr. Bowles would say, *'of giving them up, that by rest and regular treatment a cure may be performed in May - during which time something inferior may have run away with the stakes? No, keep him going as well as you can till these are over, and then, as the common people say, let 'Dr. Green' (spring grass) cure what the farrier cannot'.* Mr. Bowles possessed not only extraordinary skill in his profession, but a large fund of common sense, which recommended him to the Newmarket trainers, and many quaint sayings acceptable in all quarters. His frame of mind was religious, and, *'improving the occasion,'* as it is called, he was often heard to say, *'Let a man make himself thoroughly to understand the structure of a horse's foot, its economy, its bearings, its beauties, its provisions, and elasticity, and should he then turn and say 'There is no God' that man is a fool and liar'.'*

'To Mr. Bowles open-handed generosity and native kindliness of heart must be attributed the fact that he left but a modest fortune behind him at his death, his life-long maxim having been that 'money honestly got and well spent is the only real riches'. During his life, no one was better known on the Turf; and when he quitted it, he left no one behind more esteemed than he had been'. His standing in the profession merited a portrait by Benjamin Marshall .

John Bowles by Benjamin Marshall.

This handsome portrait of 1825 with his right hand resting on a horse's skull was reproduced as a lithograph at the time of his death in 1834. His nephew, Benjamin, who qualified at the RVC in 1826 and had worked with his uncle for seven years, succeeded him.

Just before Bowles died an article[12] in The Veterinarian bemoaned the fact that no veterinary surgeon had been able to obtain a living in Newmarket despite the fact that there were a great number of *'valuable horses at Newmarket; and at certain times of the year all the pride of the English racing breed is collected there'*. In spite of the need to keep the horses in good health, the writer reported that *'seven or eight young men have gone, one after the other, from the Veterinary College to Newmarket, and have left it in a year or two in despair and disgust'*. Apparently an old farrier *'who, it seems, has pretty well feathered his nest'*[13] and John Bowles were consulted frequently. But *'a veterinary surgeon cannot live in Newmarket'*.

A Murky Story

What was going on in Newmarket? Was there any truth in the assertions made by the unnamed author? Were there any barriers put in the way of young men who wanted to establish a business in Newmarket?

The article did set off a debate. But it was part of a longer-term debate about the future of veterinary surgery and how to improve professional standards.

As we have seen, the old-fashioned stablemen had their own remedies and felt able to look after their charges. The writer describes *'the metropolis of the [training] groom's empire; it is where he has for many a year ruled with absolute sway…The tyranny of the groom, founded, like tyranny everywhere, on ignorance and indolence, is despotic'*. It was seen as protectionism; the groom was *'jealous of a rival, and a rival whose superiority he feels and dreads…he is extremely cautious how he admits in the stable the man who will detect at a glance the errors of which he himself is beginning to be conscious, although he obstinately clings to them'*. Even the owners had to submit to this tyranny.

And the trainers wanted to guard their secrets of training and doctoring from their competitors *'with the most scrupulous care'*. A vet was a potential source of leaks. He may *'reveal a secret supposed to be well worth knowing; or he may throw discredit on a system which has been the foundation*

of the trainer's reputation and profit. In fact, vets may have been their own worst enemy by forgetting their obligation 'to see and hear, but say nothing'.

In an age of serious gambling, the sight of a vet in the yard could lead to a *'most serious and ruinous change in the odds, if it be suspected that there is anything amiss'*. And there would be those, both inside and outside the stable, who would want to profit from any titbit of information that they could glean from the vet that could be used in the betting market to the detriment of the owner or trainer. In this regard Bowles must have built up a strong reputation for discretion for him to be allowed into the confederacy of Prince's stable. Perhaps it was a benefit to be living in Cambridge away from the hotbed of gossip and intrigue in Newmarket.

To protect themselves owners and trainers would resort to subterfuge. In one case an anonymous vet visited the sick horse daily, but never at the owner's stable and never in the same place twice. In another the vet was put up in the best inn in a country town and had to walk a mile to a lonely farm to see his patient. He met one or two men who used a common name and sometimes they dined with him in the evening. His one obligation was not to ask the name of the patient, nor to mention it to anyone, if he should discover it by accident. He was paid handsomely for his silence.

The Veterinary Art

In an 1832 response to the article[14], W.J.G. commented on *'the degraded, the neglected state of the veterinary art in this country'*. It is only through *'the exertions of individuals that the veterinary art still holds rank among the professionals at all'*. W.J.G. argued for an improvement in those joining the College, suggesting that *'such men as rat-catchers, mutton pie-men, razor grinders and tinkers were being admitted to the Veterinary College'* and nothing was likely to improve as long as a *'Committee of examiners who can and do know little about the diseases of the horse and the manner of treating them and absolutely nothing at all about sheep or cattle and who are no more capable of judging the actual qualification of the pupil than Mr. Jenkins the cupper, Mr. Tomkins the dentist or Mr. St John of Harley Street'*.

It would be a surprise if a young vet could

establish himself in Newmarket because W.J.G. goes on to say 'the student leaves St. Pancras just as ignorant, as to the pedigree or performance or the pulse of the foal as the professors themselves. It is the want of knowledge that makes the veterinary surgeon appear more ignorant than perhaps he really is, and, as we all know, there is no need for that'.

Vets in Newmarket

But perhaps, more importantly, the anonymous writer had chosen the wrong town to put at the centre of a debate about the future of veterinary education and professional standing. A search of the Directories, Census Records and literature suggests that there were established veterinary practices in Newmarket. Perhaps there was a need to take more than veterinary education and qualifications into account when assessing the likely success of a business. In particular local and family links to the racing industry appear to be very important.

The first qualified vet to work in Newmarket was Thomas Attfield. He qualified on 7th July 1795 in the second batch of graduates that were passed by the College. In 1797 he is listed amongst the subscribers to Weatherby's Racing Calendar as 'Mr Attfield, Veterinary Surgeon, Newmarket'. Little is known about him. He married Miss Hart of Bury St. Edmunds on 23rd November 1797[15]. He continued as a subscriber to the Racing Calendar up to 1803, listed in Cambridgeshire in the first year and then in Suffolk thereafter[16]. He died suddenly on 7th May 1803[17]. Death denied him the opportunity to establish himself in the town.

During the course of the second Trial of Daniel Dawson, evidence was heard from Joseph Goodwin 'a veterinary surgeon, who resided in London, but who lived at Newmarket in 1809'[18]. He had been called to examine the horses being trained by J. Stevens that had been poisoned and were the subject of Dawson's second trial, although the events had occurred earlier than those in the first trial. Presumably Goodwin was one of the young men who had tried to set up in Newmarket but had failed.

Newmarket trade directories of 1823/24 and 1830 list two vets - Charles O'Connor and William Barrow[19]. O'Connor qualified from the Royal Veterinary College on 12th April 1800 and joined the 12th Dragoons. In 1808 he was placed on permanent half-pay by the Ordnance Department of the Royal Regiment of Artillery. He was still living in Mill Hill, Newmarket in 1841 aged 60 and described as 'independent'[20]. In 1834 O'Connor contributed to the debate about the efficacy of aloes from Barbados as a purgative[21].

William Barrow did not take a professional qualification but did found the Barrow Dynasty in Newmarket. His two sons qualified from the RVC - William on 28th May 1837 aged 23, and Richard two weeks later on 14th June, aged 21. Both ran the practice in partnership and described themselves as 'veterinary surgeon and farmer'. Both married daughters of trainers. William married Caroline Frances Boyce daughter of Richard Dixon Boyce and Richard married Elizabeth Neale, daughter of Henry Neale. Frances Boyce's sister, Elizabeth, married Patrick Conolly, the jockey. William, junior carried on the business until 1895. His son William became a veterinary surgeon, but did not succeed to the Newmarket business. Richard's son, George, followed him into the business and continued practicing into the twentieth century. Another of Richard's sons, Frank Arthur, set up in business as a pharmaceutical chemist in the High Street. Perhaps he became a supplier of drugs to the veterinary practice.

The Barrows had a farm near Newmarket where they stood stallions for over forty years. Amongst the stallions were Irish Birdcatcher, John O'Gaunt and Galopin. They offered the 'best accommodation (that) can be had, with loose boxes, good pasturage, private paddocks (if required) and a succession of green crops'. They added value by offering their professional services to foaling mares[22].

By 1844 there were five vets operating in the town, the two Barrows, Mary Kerry, Joseph Leech and Henry Rowe Stevens.

Mary Kerry was the widow of John Kerry who employed her brother, John Wells, to manage her husband's old business. She was succeeded by her son George, who, in turn, was succeeded by his son, George William. Mother and son were not qualified as vets but George William did qualify in 1872. George William was still operating the business in St, Mary's Square in 1926. George William's sister, Liza Turner Kerry married Frank Charles Arnull. Frank Charles was the grandson of Bill Arnull, the jockey. His two brothers became trainers in Germany and his sister married Richard Waugh, the Newmarket trainer. Frank

Charles and Liza had nine children. Of those, five became trainers, Ernest Frank in Norway, George William and Alexander Arthur in Germany, William Colledge and Frank Greenall Bland in Denmark.

The fourth vet was the locally born man, Joseph Leech, son of the horse painter, William Leech, who had married Julia Arnull, the widow of Samuel Arnull, the jockey. Joseph qualified on 6th March 1828. He died in 1847. His sisters married trainers. Juliana married William Cooper, Harriet married Edward Theakston and Elizabeth married Charles Marson.

Henry Rowe Stevens was an outsider. He qualified on 18 February 1834. His first child was born in Newmarket in 1838. He operated out of the Kingston Buildings.

He was a pillar of society in Newmarket, being the Registrar of Births, Marriages and Deaths in 1850. By 1862 he had moved to Park Lane, London.

In 1896 the Barrow and Kerry practices continue as represented by the third generation of the family. After qualification at Edinburgh in 1879, Edward Hugh Leach had established a third practice at 8, Queensberry Buildings. Leach was the brother of Felix Leach, the trainer and uncle of Jack Leach, the jockey. Edward Hugh had two sons, Robert E. and Harold Hugh, who both qualified as vets. Harold succeeded to the practice.

Practical Observation

Using practical experience and disciplined observation the Newmarket vets contributed to the development of veterinary thinking. In 1844 Richard Barrow described the effects of carcinoma of the brain and forced the President of the Veterinary Medical Association to rethink his diagnosis. The President wrote: *'I can bear testimony to Mr. Barrow being a most minute observer, a gentleman of the strictest veracity, and a practitioner of unquestionable talent. There is, therefore, in my mind, no room to doubt the correctness of the description he has favoured us with'*[23].

The Barrows were early adopters and promoters of ether as an anaesthetic for *'firing, castration and other severe operations'*[24]. The Veterinary Record entertained sanguine hopes…that this stifler of pain and sensation will one day come into common use, both for surgeons and veterinary surgeons'.

In 1856, William followed up with a detailed description of the removal of a 19 1/2 lbs. sanguineous ovarian tumour from the hack mare of a local clergyman. The mare had been ridden to the Barrow infirmary but two days later *'the animal staggered, fell and expired without a struggle'*[25].

Henry Stevens advocated the Charlier System of farriery that was developed in France and which used lightweight shoes around the front of the hoof, rather than the very heavy, close-nailed iron plates previously in use[26]. He was also an early advocate against firing and developed his own ointment which he advertised as *'the only substitute for firing horses, after twenty-five years extensive use, retains its celebrity as the safest and best remedy for curbs, splints, spavins, sore shins, diseased ligaments or tendons in the horse; it never blemishes, may be applied during work and no horse will gnaw its legs after application'*[27]. He continued to sell his ointment after he retired to Park Lane, London.

The Barrow Brothers had also developed their own competitive product, Barrow's Golden Ointment of Iodine, which again was *'the most effectual remedy for splints, ringbones, sidebones, etc. and was warranted not to blemish'*[28].

After a suspicious start the Newmarket veterinarians demonstrated their value to the trainers and owners. William Barrow almost monopolised the market. In 1879, James Rice wrote: *'there is not a trainer in the town who would for one moment hesitate to call in that gentleman, however necessary secrecy as to the precise condition of a horse might be. Trainers know to whom they trust; and Mr. Barrow, in his morning rounds, passes from stable to stable laden with knowledge for which the 'backers' and the 'bookmakers' would willingly give thousands. It is also sufficient proof of Mr. Barrow's extraordinary ability and assiduity, that in all these years no one has successfully endeavoured to wrest from him a solid share of the Newmarket business'*[29]. Prince Batthyany was so impressed that he presented him with a gold tankard worth 800 guineas after Galopin won the 1875 Derby.

Sir George Chetwynd argued that things often went amiss when training racehorses and that *'if the mishap seems serious, the best veterinary surgeon available should be called in; for although the trainer may know the best treatment to be adopted under various circumstances, it is far more satisfactory to himself and to the owner of the horse (particularly so to the latter) to know that sound professional advice has been sought and adopted'*[30]. He used Mr Barrow as his best example *'his reputation extends far and wide, and his duty is always fearlessly and conscientiously done'.*

George Barrow in 1895.

His nephew George won the plaudits of King Edward VII and his trainer, Richard Marsh. Diamond Jubilee had disgraced himself in his first race as a two-year-old on the July side at Newmarket. It was decided that he should be 'added to the list' and the late Mr. George Barrow was instructed accordingly. Mr. Barrow found certain difficulties that would not have deterred a younger vet. Diamond Jubilee was reprieved. He went on to win the Triple Crown and was ultimately sold to Senor Ignacio Correas for 30,000 guineas[31].

Edward Leach qualified from Edinburgh in 1879 and was made a fellow of the RCVS in 1886. He established his reputation in Newmarket by saving the racing career of one of Lord Falmouth's fillies that was trained by Mathew Dawson. Her legs curved inwards. Leach thought he could do something. Dawson remarked *'You can't make crooked legs straight'. 'No, but I think I can do something by shoeing, and, at any rate, make the filly of some use for racing purposes'.* The exercise was successful and the filly went onto win a race for them[32]. His two sons, Robert E. and Hugh H., both qualified as vets. Hugh was still practicing out of Derby House, Exning Road in 1926.

The original Leach residence and surgery was at The Chestnuts on Exeter Road just by the Clock Tower. The site eventually became a garage, but a reminder of its former use came a few years ago when an ointment pot marked 'Leach, F.R.C.V.S. Newmarket' was found in the hydraulic lift pit.

Ointment Jar of Edward Leach: courtesy S.W.Ricketts.

The pit probably housed the lift for the original Newmarket equine operating table.

The family ties between the veterinary profession and the racing industry continued to be strong to the end of the nineteenth century. Edward Leach's younger brother, Felix, followed him to Newmarket. After a chance meeting with Mathew Dawson on Newmarket Heath Felix became Dawson's assistant trainer, then partner and eventually went on his own as a trainer[33]. Felix's son, Jack, became a jockey. He became a trainer after difficulties maintaining his riding weight. After he retired he became a racing journalist with The Observer.

Alexander Adam Waugh was the third son of James Waugh, the trainer. Alexander was born in 1862. After he passed his exams he joined his father and brother William in Hungary where they worked for Prince Festetics. William returned to Newmarket to train for Sir Blundell Maple at Falmouth House. Alexander took the job of stud vet at Childwickbury in Hertfordshire, the stud farm of Sir Blundell Maple. In 1919, William returned to Newmarket after a spell at Kingsclere in Berkshire. He took over Zetland Lodge and renamed it Balaton Lodge after the Hungarian Lake. In 1984 Balaton Lodge became the headquarters of the Animal Health Trust.

And Frederick W. Day came to Newmarket in 1894. He was a qualified vet and a racehorse trainer, who had spent some time out in Australia. He trained the winner of the Oaks (1898 Airs And Graces) and the Two Thousand Guineas (1901 Handicapper). His son, Reginald, started as trainer when he was 17 years old in 1899. Before taking over from his father in 1912, Reg spent time at the Graditz Stud in Germany training for the Kaiser. He took that job over from Richard Waugh. Richard's brother-in-law had married the daughter of George Kerry whose son George William Kerry, was the Newmarket vet. Very intermingled.

Whatever the truth of the 1831 editorial in The Veterinarian, the veterinary profession did succeed in Newmarket. The primary reason must have been professional competence. The work of the Barrow Brothers was marked by close observation and measurement and a willingness to adopt new techniques, such as the use of ether. The ability to keep his mouth shut propelled William Barrow to a near monopoly of business. In many ways he was the true heir to John Bowles.

But there were other reasons for success. Subscribing to the annual Racing Calendar will have endeared Thomas Attwood to the racing community. The marriages of the Barrow Brothers and Joseph Leech into racing families will have helped overcome many of the early objections that these newly qualified vets lacked practical knowledge of horses. Coming from the local community was an added bonus. As an outsider Henry Stevens took on the job of Registrar to integrate himself into the town. The vets had overcome 'the tyranny of the groom'.

By 1900 there were six vets working in Newmarket. Amongst them was William Livock, who had qualified at Edinburgh. By 1912 he had bought March House on the High Street. It was there that he established his practice, which in turn became the dominant veterinary practice in the Twentieth Century until Peter Rossdale challenged it in 1959.

Acknowlegments

I would like to acknowledge the help in preparing this essay from Simon Jackson and Frances Houston of the Royal Veterinary College, Clare Boulton of the Royal College of Veterinary Surgeons and Jochem Heicke of Berlin.

References
1   Kent, J. (1893), Racing Life of Lord George Cavendish Bentinck, M. P. London: p. 36.
2   Weatherby, Edward and James (1812), The Racing Calendar for the year 1811. London: p. 23.
3   Kent, J. (1893), Racing Life of Lord George Cavendish Bentinck, M. P. London: p. 36.
4   Ibid, p.37.
5   The Druid (1856), The Post and The Paddock (Revised and re-edited edition). London: p. 167.
6   Kent, J. (1893), Racing Life of Lord George Cavendish Bentinck, M. P. London: p. 35.
7   Kent, G. (1812), The Extraordinary Trial of Daniel Dawson. Newmarket: p. 28.
8   Kent, J. (1893), Racing Life of Lord George Cavendish Bentinck, M. P. London: p. 36.
9   The Veterinarian August 1st 1831 Vol. IV #44 p455
10 Anon (1834), Death of Mr John Bowles, Sporting Magazine, Vol. 8 second series pp351-352
11 Rice, J. (1879), History of the British Turf. London: Vol. 1, pp170-172.
12 The Veterinarian August 1st 1831 Vol. IV #44 p455
13 Ibid p458
14 W. J. G. (1832), The Veterinarian, February 1st 1832 Vol. V #50 pp88 - 92

15 The Monthly Magazine or British Register (1797), Volume 4, p. 473

16 Weatherby, Edward and James, The Racing Calendars for the years 1797 - 1803. London: Subscriber lists

17 Gentleman's Magazine (1804), Volume 95, p. 486.

18 Kent, G. (1812), The Second Trial and Capital Conviction of Daniel Dawson. London: p.15.

19 Pigot and Co. (1830), National Commercial Directory (facsimile edition). London: p. 38

20 The National Archives: 1841 Census Records, Ref: HO 107/1027/15

21 Percival, W. (1834), Hippopathology: a treatise on the disorders and lameness of the horse. London: p. 109.

22 Weatherby, Edward and James (1850), The Racing Calendars for the year 1850. London:

23 Barrow, R. (1845), A case of carcinoma in the brain of a horse, Veterinary Record and Transactions of the Veterinary Medical Association, Volume 1, p83.

24 Barrow, M. (1847), Experiments with aether, The Veterinary Record, Volume III, p. 116.

25 Barrow, W. (1856), A sanguineous ovarian tumour, The Veterinarian, Volume XXIX - Volume II, Fourth Series, p. 255.

26 Rance, C. (2009), Stevens's Ointment for Horses, quoted from The Era (London) Sat 23rd February 1862 (http://thequackdoctor.com/index.php/stevenss-ointment-for-horses)

27 [Advertisement] (1850): Journal of the Royal Agricultural Society of England, Volume II, p. 13.

28 [Advertisement] (1849): Ruff's Guide to the Turf (Spring) p. 202

29 Rice, J. (1879), History of the British Turf. London: Volume II, pp. 213-214.

30 Chetwynd, Sir George (1891), Racing Reminiscences and Experience of the Turf. London: Volume I, p. 116.

31 Allison, W. (1922), Memories of Men and Horses. London: p. 209

32 Humphris, E. M. (1928), Life of Mathew Dawson. London: p. 132.

33 Leach, J. (1970), A Rider on the Stand. London: p26

Chapter 4

Headquarters did not exist, We had to invent it

by: Alan Medlock

Alan Medlock was born in Coventry in 1944. He joined Total Oil (GB) Limited, in 1963 after being educated in Rugby. In 1975 he joined the West Midlands County Council Trading Standards Department and transferred to Coventry University, in 1979. In 1990 he became a licensee and ran his own business until 2000 when he joined the Jockey Club Rooms, as Rooms Steward. His background is in sales, marketing and general management. He was on the Finance Committee of the National Union of Students, a director of its sales company from 1980 to 1990, and a founder member and secretary of the buying consortium for university and college bars throughout the UK.

The Pilgrims Way.

In ancient times, who would have thought that land along the side of the road from Cambridge to Norwich would become so important? This road intersected the Icknield Way and was an important trading route, one of the four major highways in England consisting of the Fosse Way, Ermine Street and Watling Street. The road was said to be named after the Iceni tribe, who may have used it as a trading route between East Anglia and Wessex.

The peoples of Exning and Wood Ditton realised the trading potential of this location as pilgrims and travellers passed along this religious route and that no one was servicing their needs. Therefore, by moving a short distance, a thriving community was set up and the first chapter in the tale began.

A charter was purchased from King John in the 1200s to hold markets and fairs. The town of Novum Mercatum was established and grew in size and importance. With the increase in numbers of travellers, particularly pilgrims visiting shrines in both Norwich and Walsingham, and the holding of regular markets and fairs it soon surpassed and outgrew the original hamlets.

Racing, But not as we know it.

Horse racing and breeding have been carried out in this country for many hundreds of years with the earliest recorded meetings dating back to 1511 and 1530 at Chester and York respectively. However, racing is much older than this. The major events were linked to the aristocracy and members of the Royal Court with meetings taking place where and when the court was in residence. But there were also numerous annual meetings at various towns around the country, many linked to local fairs and holidays. Races for the Court were often run on a match basis over a distance of some four miles and at local meetings some races were run in heats, the horses being rubbed down and rested between events. Many horses were ridden by their owners or by friends and some by jockeys, who, unlike today, were a motley band of what could be called, "riding grooms", often unkempt and sometimes dishonest men, who were known to bet on rival horses, pull their own mounts and generally cheat during the race. The truth was that there were no proper rules and sanctions against these miscreants and the format of the races, cross-country gallops, allowed for the misdemeanours to go unpunished.

King James 1.

There was little change to the town until King James I of England and VI of Scotland decided to decamp from London during the summer months to escape the smells and claustrophobia of the capital. Complete with his entourage and courtiers, he set out to find an environment to enable him to pursue his country pursuits of hawking, hare coursing and riding horses. He arrived at Newmarket, no longer called Novum Mercatum, and set up his headquarters at the Griffin Inn, purchased for £400, and used the lands between Exning and Thetford for his sporting activities. He transferred his attentions to hunting on the Heath and commissioned Sir Robert Vernon to loose 50 brace of partridge and the same number of hares every year. Match racing soon followed and the first recorded race was in 1622; this was a £100 bet between a horse belonging to Lord Salisbury and a sorrel, named Prince, belonging to the Marquis of Buckingham.

Six miles to go (watercolour) by James Power.

Newmarket Heath.

The early 1600's were the time that Newmarket became the sporting second home of Royalty and indeed James and his courtiers spent more time than was suitable in the town and on the Heath. Both Buckingham and Salisbury and many of his other favourites upset a parliament, fast showing its puritan tendency, with the protracted absences from London pursuing their favoured country pursuits. It has often puzzled me as to whether he set out for Newmarket, or having followed the road, arrived at this destination after a days travel. Should this have been the case, then I have thought that if the road infrastructure and conditions had been better and carriages softer and better sprung, then where would he have finished up and where would we be now.

James was the first of the monarchs to declare an affinity with the area and the start of racing horses in this area had begun. It was King Charles II who established the town as racing and sporting venue and his sponsorship gave rise to considerable development, with the construction of a new palace between the Rutland Hotel and Sun Lane in 1672, particularly as the old palace, which was unused and ransacked during the Commonwealth, was too small and unsuitable for his purposes.

In addition to the courtiers, he had a considerable

retinue of followers, who would all need lodgings, stables, feeding and bedding and this demand was instrumental in continuing the development of the town.

Jockey Club Members.

We have still as yet to encounter the good men of the Jockey Club and it is not for some time that they appeared, or at least are recorded has having done so in their own right. They existed as a group in London, frequenting various hostelries, choosing to move or being moved from place to place. A popular trend during this period was for the group to have a name and their chosen identity was derived from their status as horse owners and some time riders and should not be confused with the modern accepted interpretation. They arrived, in the town around 1752 and having had various meeting places in the High Street acquired premises, a Coffee House, which became known as the Jockey Club Rooms. These premises solved lots of their problems because, not only did it provide them with a settled location, it enabled them to store their wager books in safety and its very permanence reinforced their identity and credibility. They used these facilities, as their Newmarket base, but also had rooms in Mr. Tattersall's horse repository at Hyde Park Corner in London, which were not opened until 1766.

Rules of Racing.

The prominence of the Jockey Club, as a rule maker and arbiter came about because of the type of racing at that time and the mismatches with the uncertainty of age and weights and general disputes about riding practices. There were rules for the King's Plate that were inappropriate for all other races and Newmarket rules, half of which related to the conduct of betting. What were lacking were rules consistently applied and an authority to whom appeals could be made and whose decision was final. The Jockey Club had organizational skills and a membership list to be reckoned with and they very quickly assumed the mantle. In 1757, a dispute at the Curragh was referred to the club and in 1758 it published its first general order relating to the penalties relating to the non-declaration of overweight.

This single act was the beginning of the transformation from the "Drinking Club" into the governing body of racing. Whether or not this had always been the intention, it was now showing its strength and flexing its muscles.

In 1762 a second order was issued relating to the use of registered colours and 19 noblemen and gentlemen, being members, registered colours, which they agreed would be used consistently; but it was the make up of the group that gave credence to the power of the Club within racing. It comprised a Royal Duke, five other Dukes, a Marquis, five Earls, a Viscount and a Baron.

The Jockey Club.

The Jockey Club was on its way and even at this time reference was made to the Stewards and the development of a management and organizational structure. It was necessary to have a focal point and someone to hold everything together and consequently we saw the appointment of Sir Charles Bunbury, in 1768, as the "The First Great Dictator of the Turf". Bunbury assumed the role at the age of 28 and did much to organize and change many of the established racing traditions. He was opposed to the running of long distance races and introduced shorter ones carrying lighter weights to encourage speed over stamina.

Ready for some sport (watercolour) by James Power.

The period from the late 1700s through the 1800s was hugely important not only to Newmarket but the racing industry and community as a whole. Among many developments we saw the introduction of a governing body to organise and structure racing, the development and patronage of racecourses, the emergence of the "Thoroughbred Horse", the move to licensed jockeys

and the establishment of training yards.

July Course (Oils) By James Power. Courtesy of Drs Simon and Elizabeth Bailey.

With the Jockey Club located in the High Street it was a natural consequence that the town would see the benefits of this patronage. There are many properties still standing, which bear the names of prominent early members, although they are no longer used as housing. This coupled with the decision to base themselves here and more importantly, to keep their horses here, made significant differences to the economic and employment prospects in the town. In the early days, many of the gentlemen had lodgings in the area and took their horses backwards and forwards to their main homes, meaning that from time to time the town would be full and at other times empty. The Jockey Club would have a major influence in the future of the town and the establishment of a culture and industry centred on horse racing.

Influence on the Town.

The permanence that their presence created and the service industry that grew up in the area was undoubtedly a significant factor in what we now take as part and parcel of daily life in Newmarket. The decision to build houses and keep great numbers of horses here meant that the town developed a more secure future and the investment in money and jobs, together with the introduction of stables and their employment prospects dramatically, altered the landscape of the whole area. A new economy was built on the back of this activity. We can see the introduction of stables and training, breeding establishments, farriers, veterinary practitioners, jockeys, horse sales and last but by no means least, the general public. All these people were beneficiaries of the decision by the Jockey Club to house itself in the town.

Not only did we witness a change in the fortunes of Newmarket, we saw dramatic differences in the style and type of racing. Following on from Bunbury's initiatives and the gradual shortening of distances, it was no longer deemed good practice to race from Fleym Dyke, a distance of 8 miles, or 6 miles from Six Mile Bottom, back to the finish. The emphasis on distance and stamina changed and with it more thought was given to the welfare of the horse.

Courses for Horses.

By 1822 there were at least 18 courses that were used for different matches and horses of specific ages. These varied in length from the Yearling Course of 2 furlongs and 147 yards for colts a year old to The Beacon Course, at 4 miles 1 furlong and 168 yards, for 5 year olds and older. Many of these became obsolete with the shortening distances and nowadays we have only the 2 courses: The Rowley Mile Course and the July Course. The Rowley Mile uses a section of the Beacon Course, which itself was part of the original Long Course that dates from the early seventeenth century. The Rowley Mile is named after King Charles II's favourite hack, 'Old Rowley'. The July Course is used for summer racing and is the last part of the Round Course set up by Charles II in 1665.

During the 18th Century sweepstakes and invitation races gradually took over from match racing and heat races. More and more named and titled events were introduced to the racing calendar.

In 1776 Anthony St. Leger and his friend Charles Watson-Wentworth, 2nd Marquis of Rockingham, organised a subscription race for three-year-olds over two miles with a purse of 25 guineas. It was contested by 5 horses, the colts carrying 8 stones and the fillies, 7 stone 12 pounds. This soon became known as the St. Leger and was the first of the championship races known as the Classics. The distance has been shortened to 1 mile 6 furlongs and 132 yards and is now run over the Town Moor course, not the original Cantley Common course.

Newmarket Landmark Clock Tower (watercolour) by James Power.
The Clock Tower is placed at the top of the High Street.. Local builder Richard Arber built it to commemorate Queen Victoria's Diamond Jubilee of 1887. The tower was paid for by public subscription but local trainer Charles Blanton donated the clock itself which was made by Smiths of Derby. The tower was opened officially in 1890.

The next initiative was on 12th May 1779 when Lord Derby and his friends, including Sir Charles Bunbury and other luminaries from Newmarket, ran a race for fillies over one and a half miles. There were 17 subscribers for this 50 guineas race, which became known as The Oaks. The Derby followed in 1780, a race for three year old colts and fillies over one mile, later extended to a mile and a half. Not only were these races organised by the members of the Jockey Club, but also their officials were used. Officiating at the 1780 Derby were Mr. Hilton, the Newmarket judge, assisted by Mr. Samuel Betts, the Jockey Club starter. Further Newmarket has contributed to the continuous running of these races by hosting them during the First and Second World Wars.

The remaining two Classic races are both run at Newmarket. They are the Two Thousand Guineas, first run in 1809 over a distance of one mile, and the One Thousand Guineas, first run in 1814 over the same distance. Both races have been run continuously, although during the last conflict they were run over the July course, because the Rowley Mile was used as an airfield.

Breeding.

From the mid-seventeenth century, great changes took place in the breeding of racehorses. For many years the breeding of racehorses had been carried out predominantly in the Vale of York. Eastern blood had always been involved, but after 1680 dramatic changes took place. Arabians, Barbs and Turks were mated with the few imported mares and the cream of the mares of this country. By 1750, around 150 stallions had been imported from the Middle East. This initiative created the Thoroughbred breed and to this day almost all thoroughbred foals can trace their ancestry in a direct male line back to one of the three main imports; the Byerley Turk, foaled around 1680, the Darley Arabian (1700) and the Godolphin Arabian (1724). It was this development that opened up the industry. As the format and style of racing changed, so the horse was selectively bred to mature earlier and to emphasize speed over stamina.

Trainers and Training.

A major aspect, in the development of "Headquarters", was the introduction of trainers and training establishments. Tregonwell Frampton, Keeper of the Running Horses for Queen Anne, was one of the first to train on the Heath. He used the proxy of the Queen, who was disinterested in Newmarket, to arbitrate on events and races on the Heath until his dismissal by King

George I. He was a notorious gambler, jockey and cock fighting enthusiast and made many challenges on behalf of the monarch, but as he was able to manipulate the conditions in his owner's favour and interpret the rules as he saw fit, they were not always taken up.

The members of the Jockey Club owned many of the training establishments and they employed individuals to look after their horses. However, by the 1850's many yards were in the hands of individuals, who had been successful in racing and graduated to becoming a trainer in their own right. Their methods were as different as their backgrounds coming through the ranks as jockeys, grooms and, in some cases, by patronage, some adopting airs and graces, because of their change of status that did not always endear them to their colleagues.

A gradual change occurred at about this time and the training of horses began to be a more accepted profession and the calibre of the individuals was noted within the industry. Comments were expressed not only about the conduct and education of the trainers but also about their integrity and honesty. Training methods were altered fundamentally to take into account the welfare and care of horses. At one time, it was considered good practice to work horses in head, body and breast sweaters, after allowing a horse to become gross before they went into training. This would require the horse to be sweated and purged and at times being put into something akin to a sauna. The sweat would then be removed by scraping with a strigel almost to the point of bleeding and then the horse would be rugged up and hooded. This activity would be carried out twice a week. A much more enlightened and individual approach was adopted towards the horses and by the mid 1800's a much more caring attitude prevailed.

Veterinary Practice and Development.

In view of the attitudes and strange notions that existed with regard to the care and welfare of horses, the position of veterinary practitioner did not exist until the late 1700's. Much of the medicine and care for the racing stock was handed down from father to son or groom to groom and the term quackery may have been appropriate. The death of Eclipse coincided with the birth of veterinary science in this country. When the horse died it was desirable to find out the cause of death and if possible the reasons for his phenomenal success. There were no qualified veterinarians, nor was there a veterinary school in this country and it was Charles Vial de Saint Bel, a graduate of Lyons, Europe's first veterinary school, who provided the answer. He was in England at this time and it is possibly due to these events that a college was set up in London in 1791, admitting its first students in January 1792.

Since that date the professional care of animals and in particular racehorses has developed dramatically and it is for this reason that the town now boasts three world class equine hospitals and testing laboratories and is recognised as one of the leading sites in this field. It has not been easy for veterinarians to practice in Newmarket and their acceptance by the racing industry has been hard fought and won.

In the 1830s it was extremely difficult for them to even earn a living, because of the established power base of the grooms and farriers, who were the traditional "doctors" and held total control over the yards with regards to treating horses. It was reported in 'The Veterinarian' August, 1831, that many of the masters of the yards were in awe and sometimes held to ransom by these individuals who held a monopoly for treatment and were certainly not about to give up their lucrative trade, particularly to a new profession where young men were appearing in the town with a certificate from a college, but to their mind, no experience or knowledge of horses and their ailments.

It is also important to understand the structure of racing in those days as it is far removed from that of today. Racing was steeped in secrecy, as betting was a more significant part of the revenue than prize money. It was, therefore, imperative that the welfare and general well being of any of the horses was kept within the confines of the yard and in some cases, only the individual groom and owner had the information. It was easy for the established practitioners to trade on this situation and as loyal and honourable people with years of unblemished service to the masters and yards, the position of the newly 'born' veterinarian was going to be difficult.

Many of the early veterinarians left the town, because they were unable to earn a living and many of those that stayed operated at times in secret. They were asked to treat horses at strange venues and to keep the identity of the animal secret. This was done, in many cases, to save the

owner/master of the horse from having to answer to the groom and farrier, as to why he had gone outside the accepted circle for advice. Fortunately, the situation changed and progressed and the industry settled down and embraced the veterinary practitioners. However, was this due to their professionalism, qualifications and knowledge or the changes that were happening within racing? Once the structure and format changed and the emphasis on betting dwindled, there was not quite the same need for the over bearing secrecy that had existed before and the veterinarians were able to operate on a level playing field with the established grooms and farriers. They were able to prove that their expertise was superior and consequently their positions were guaranteed in the town.

Over the years, the Jockey Club has recognised the importance of the profession to racing by appointing a veterinary officer and a committee consisting of senior members and veterinary officers to ensure that the appropriate care and welfare of thoroughbred horses is maintained and developed.

Sellers.

As with racing and breeding, changes were made with the selling of horses. Mr. Richard Tattersall, the founder of the company, had started his sales ring at Hyde Park Corner in 1766 on land belonging to Lord Grosvenor. The property developed, not only for horse sales, but also to host the members, of the Jockey Club in two elegantly furnished rooms, where they held their meetings. The business prospered and developed and allowed the family to venture into breeding and the wholesale purchases of horses and studs. He was active in matching all the mares bred from Eclipse that he could acquire with his own great stallion, Highflyer. He eventually purchased a farm property near Ely and built a residence called Highflyer Hall.

The move to Newmarket and the introduction of sales is recorded in 1825, with Richard Tattersall, the grandson of the founder, selling horses outside the Rooms and is an obvious consequence of the move by the Jockey Club members, to the town. In the period, between 1860 and 1870, the Company leased land and paddocks behind Queensberry House. In 1884 Mr. Tattersall purchased more paddocks from the executors of the late Sir Richard Wallace and developed the present establishment.

The statue of Hyperion was erected, in front of the Coffee Room, in March, 1996, having been moved from its previous home near Woodlands Stud, Snailwell Road. The statue was left to the Jockey Club, by the late Lord Derby, in his will, when he died in November, 1994.
The Coffee Room dates back to the 1750's and was the first home of the gentlemen, of the Jockey Club having had various headquarters in London and Newmarket. The frontage was remodelled in the 1830's and then again in 1933, which is the current façade. photos by courtesy Trevor Jones.

Modern Times.

It is not appropriate for the writer to speculate as to what would have happened had the Jockey Club not decided to put down roots in this town, but the picture would not be the same as it is today. The industries that have been built and nurtured because of its presence have contributed to the prosperity and the development of the region. Not only have the associated businesses been the beneficiaries of this decision, but also the Club itself has prospered and grown by virtue of its own peculiar status.

The Jockey Club, now no longer fulfilling the role that it held in the 1850s, can, in accordance with its objectives in its Royal Charter, continue to use its influence and assets to further the interests of horseracing. All the profits generated by its commercial interests are invested in the sport. There are two elements to Jockey Club activities today: Jockey Club Racecourses and Jockey Club Estates.

Jockey Club Racecourses is responsible for the operation of fourteen racecourses and a catering partnership. The Racecourse division was formed in 1964 with the objective of securing the future of racecourses for horseracing. Its trustee ownership of the group ensures that all profits are re-invested in racing.

Jockey Club Estates.

Jockey Club Estates is the property and land management company, responsible for the management of 4500 acres at Newmarket and 550 acres at Lambourn. There is also a considerable property portfolio within the company including the Jockey Club Rooms, the original home of the Jockey Club in Newmarket. As with all the companies in the group, profits are re-invested into improving and developing facilities under its management. In the early days the Jockey Club held no land or property in its own right; however, over the years it has acquired considerable freehold and leasehold racing and training grounds, being the recipient of bequests and gifts of land to hold in trust for the racing industry.

The Jockey Club, over the years, was instrumental in the organisation of care and conditions for staff working in the racing and breeding industry. It set up the charity, Racing Welfare, to support and assist individuals and their dependants, if they are in need. Racing Welfare relies on donations from the racing community and since its formation in 2001 has developed into the foremost welfare agency within the industry.

Another arm of the Jockey Club in the town is the National Stud. Acquired in 2008, the Stud has a commitment to preserve the heritage of Thoroughbred breeding and provide training and education to match the aspirations of the industry. It also provides access for the public as a tourist attraction and education facility. This has also brought about a closer cooperation between the family of businesses in Newmarket and the development and changes will, it is hoped, prove beneficial to all concerned.

The benefits and opportunities that have occurred by virtue of the adoption of Newmarket by the Jockey Club can be witnessed throughout the area. There is a considerable industry reliant on the racing and breeding community and these benefits are essential to the economic and employment prospects of many people.

As I have already mentioned, the support services for the racing industry of veterinary practitioners, insurance agencies, farriers, feed suppliers, agricultural machinery suppliers, equipment and transport companies have all been beneficiaries of the development and choice of Newmarket by the Jockey Club. The most important recipients of this, however, are the people directly employed by the trainers and breeders and everyone from stable lads, jockeys, valets, agents, handlers to general factotums, who thanks to the farsightedness of the Jockey Club, are maintaining the traditions and development of the home and headquarters of racing.

Chapter 5

Origins of the Newmarket Equine Hospital

by: Richard Greenwood MA Vet MB MRCVS

*R**ichard Greenwood qualified from Cambridge University in 1964. After two years in general practice, he worked in the Hunter Valley, Australia for three years in thoroughbred stud practice with Murray Bain, a great pioneer. Returning to the UK he joined the Newmarket practice under Fred Day and Bob Crowhurst. He became a partner in 1973 and was senior partner from 1991 to 2003.*

His particular interests were in stud medicine and he collaborated in clinical trials with Professor Twink Allen and the development of ultrasound scanning. He was veterinary surgeon to Henry Cecil during a period when the stable trained no less than 21 classic winners. He was Veterinary Advisor to the Thoroughbred Breeders Association.

An article in the Veterinarian of August 1st 1831 observed *'that no veterinary surgeon had been able to obtain a living at Newmarket'. The author blamed this on his view that 'The tyranny of the groom, founded like tyranny everywhere, on ignorance and indolence, is despotic'.*

However, according to Kelly's Directory by 1900 there were 30 racehorse trainers and 6 vets in Newmarket. These included William Livock, an Edinburgh graduate and Fred 'Bushranger' Day, the grandfather of Fred Day, so named because he had been vet to the Governor of New South Wales in Sydney before coming to Newmarket.

By 1912 Livock had moved into March House, a large Georgian house, on the High Street. The premises covered nearly 2 acres and included a forge, still present, a large coach house built in 1852 and 13 loose boxes.

During the Great War, Livock was heavily involved in selecting horses to go to France. He hoped his son would join him, but all he wanted to do was 'fly and play cricket', so he joined the Naval Air Service and subsequently had a distinguished career in the Royal Air Force.

In 1923 he was joined by Brayley Reynolds. Reynolds, born in 1879, was the son of a veterinary surgeon based in Daventry. At the outbreak of the Boer War he lied about his age to join Lord Chesham's Yeomanry and fought as a trooper in South Africa. On demobilisation he had to earn a living as a veterinary assistant to fund his way through the Royal Veterinary College. He eventually qualified in 1912, aged 33 and joined the teaching staff at the college.

In 1915 Reynolds joined the Royal Veterinary Corps which grew to over 1000 vets during the Great War. He served in France and then commanded the veterinary hospital in Baghdad. This gave him vast experience and he received the OBE. At the end of the war his unit had to put down 10,000 horses. He used this opportunity to do much experimental surgery.

He developed a special technique for the laryngeal ventriculectomy operation, which was used in the practice till the 1980s when the tieback was developed. He considered Hobday a plagiarist and in the practice the operation was always called the 'Williams' or roaring operation. After the war in 1919 he was appointed Professor of *Materia Medica* at the RVC and head of the horse clinic.

His great experience and scientific approach led to much consultation work. He was also very keen on racing and in 1923 he moved to Newmarket and joined William Livock's practice in the High Street. Livock retired in 1926 and lived at and managed the racecourse stables at the Links. Geoff Leader, member of a famous Newmarket training family joined Reynolds in partnership. In 1937 they were joined by Bob Crowhurst recently qualified at the age of 21. Bob came from a dynasty of vets based in Kent, his father was a great friend of Brayley Reynolds. Both consulted regularly and travelled round the country, Brayley in a Lagonda with driver. Both were great cheese connoisseurs and used to exchange any interesting cheeses they came across by means of railway parcels.

On the outbreak of war Bob joined the Royal Veterinary Corps. In the winter of 1940 he accompanied a division of Yeoman Cavalry to

Palastine, taking 11000 horses across France by rail and then from Marseilles to Haifa by sea. After all this effort they did not see any action apart from polo, racing and jackal hunting as the division was mechanised for the North Africa campaign. The horses were retrained and used for transport and dock work. Bob went with the army on the illfated Greek expedition and only escaped using his boyhood experience by sailing a small boat with 6 others to Crete.

March House renamed Reynolds House, The Forge and Burchley House.

During the Italian campaign large numbers of mules were used for transport and Bob commanded veterinary hospitals at Bari and Persano and set up an experimental unit to study the treatment for Epizootic Lymphangitis. He ended the war as a Lt Colonel and was awarded the OBE.

Racehorse numbers were much reduced during the 2nd World War and the Classics were held at Newmarket as part of a reduced centralised racing programme.

When the war ended Fred Day joined the practice. Fred had qualified in 1935. His father Reg Day was a successful trainer from Terrace House on the High Street, now the headquarters of Tattersalls. He had trained for the Kaiser in Berlin before the 1st World War and won the German Derby 3 times.

Fred Day had worked with Sir John Hammond at the ARC Unit in Cambridge on equine fertility. He worked out and published the estrous and ovulation cycle of the horse in Welsh ponies, which is now the basis of much stud work. During the war he worked on cattle infertility and A.I. He brought this expertise in equine reproduction to Newmarket joining Brayley Reynolds in 1945. Bob Crowhurst returned in 1946 after spending a year in Lexington at Claiborne Stud under Caslick and Dymock. Their expertise particularly in the control of uterine infection combined with Day's work on the estrous cycle helped to start a revolution in stud practice. This was accelerated in the 1950s when Alycidon went to stud at Lord Derby's Woodlands Stud. The horse proved subfertile and Fred found out that his fertility could be much improved by covering close to ovulation.

Lord Derby went over to Lexington and boasted that his vet could raise a stallion's fertility by 30%. Bill McGhee was promptly sent over by Hagyards practice to find out what was being done. Of course this only worked on certain subfertile stallions, but it led to an increase in follicle examination of mares before covering and eventually to the present situation in which stallions can cover such large books of mares.

Brayley Reynolds retired from active practice in 1950. He must have been a remarkable man. His obituaries all refer to him as one of the greatest veterinary surgeons of this century. He was obviously a very strong character and did not suffer fools gladly. *"He considered sound advice to be often of more value than drugs"* and *'he took great pains to arrive at a diagnosis and was cautious with therapy'*. Two philosophies which survive in the practice today. At his retirement party at the Jockey Club Rooms a barrel of Colchester Oysters was served as a special treat. Unfortunately it resulted in food poisoning for half the great and the good of Newmarket.

Peter Rossdale joined as an assistant in 1954. He started much clinical research but left to set up his own practice in 1959, amidst much bitterness. however, it was inevitable and beneficial for all that Newmarket should have more than one practice.

Donald Simpson joined the practice in 1962 and took on the work at the National Stud which moved to Newmarket in 1963. His greatest contribution came in 1977 when the previously unrecognised Contagious Equine Metritis infection arrived in Newmarket with mares from Ireland. Donald worked out that the site of carrier status for this and other venereal diseases was the clitoris of the mare and the urethral fossa of the stallion. Swabbing of these sites is now the basis of the stud Code of Practice.

Robin McEnery, a charismatic and forward looking Irishman joined in 1964. As well as being a very knowledgeable horseman, he was an adventurous surgeon and introduced many new techniques. He left in 1974 to become a full time bloodstock agent.

From the seventies there was much expansion of the industry in Newmarket. Tattersalls moved headquarters from London and expanded the bloodstock sales, which had been at Doncaster. The British Bloodstock Agency moved up from London followed by several others.

David Ellis and Richard Greenwood became Partners in the mid seventies. Richard had spent 3 years in Scone in the Hunter Valley, New South Wales gaining valuable experience working for Murray Bain a very dynamic Scotsman, who had been a colleague of Bob Crowhurst's in the RVC in Palastine. A pioneer of stud medicine in Australia, he kept meticulous records and published many practical papers based on these records. Both practices since that time regularly exchange assistants to gain experience in their respective stud seasons.

One of the best features of the practice then and now was that everyone worked out of the same large office. Most evenings we gathered together after evening stables and there was no better education than listening to Fred and Bob discussing the day's cases and benefitting from their huge experience. Both were excellent and decisive diagnosticians, but not afraid to admit uncertainty, await developments and avoid the trap of rushing to judgement prematurely.

Veterinary work steadily expanded. In 1983 we purchased the house next door to expand the laboratory. Previously, apart from basic bacteriology all laboratory work was done at the Animal Health Trust with whom we worked closely, but they had made Jim Atherton their Chief Technician redundant. So we developed a full laboratory service and employed Jim to run it. When he retired Margaret Blackett also from the AHT joined and manages the laboratory today.

Up until the 80's, Newmarket vets could specialise in both stud and racehorse practice.The workload was more seasonal with concentration on stud work in the spring and then increasing stable work in the summer as the racing season led to trainers seeking reasons/'excuses' for unsoundness or poor performance. Then in the autumn there was a steady increase in sales work especially when Tattersalls moved their yearling sales from Doncaster to Newmarket in 1968.

The Maktoums from Dubai arrived in the early eighties leading to a big expansion in horse numbers which had been going down in the seventies.

On the stud side, improved drugs to control the estrous cycle in mares were developed and ultra-

sound scanning for pregnancy diagnosis became available. Both were pioneered in collaboration with Twink Allen from the Agriculture Research Council (ARC) station in Cambridge and the Equine Fertility Unit when he moved to Newmarket in 1989. With the horses in training, flexible endoscopes, ultrasound scans, much improved radiology and improved blood testing led to an increase in work.

Brayley Reynolds in RVC uniform after WW1.

Bone screw and plate equipment (ASIF for fracture repair and particularly arthroscopic joint surgery, in which David Ellis specialised, increased the surgical caseload. Improvements in technique and postoperative monitoring gave better survival rates with colic surgery and Huw Neal worked tirelessly on this. All this led to a need for improved surgical facilities. The old combined knock down and operating theatre with in floor, pit based hydraulic table (state of the art when it was built in the sixties) was extended to give a separate clean orthopaedic theatre with mobile table. Subsequently in 1995 the whole unit was upgraded to two clean theatres with separate knockdown/recovery rooms and preparation areas.

Up to this time we had done some referral work, but had not sought it out. However, in 1996 Ian Wright was made redundant by the AHT and he joined us, which meant building more boxes increasing the number from 20+ to 30+ on a site of just under 2 acres in the middle of town. So by the end of the nineties we had twenty five vets. James Crowhurst had joined when his father retired in the mid eighties. Andrew Edgar, Huw Neal, David Dugdale, Benoit Herinckx and Charlie Smith were partners, plus assistants and house surgeons. Mark Hillyer a specialist in Internal Medecine joined from Bristol University in 2002.

No account would be complete without mention of Mary Finch. Mary joined the practice aged 16 straight from secretarial college in 1947. She retired 50 years later in 1997. Her life was dedicated to running the office, which she did with meticulous care and integrity, setting standards of service which were an example to all.

Although there were excellent facilities on the High Street site, we were bursting at the seams and needed to expand further. Three different hospitals close to the town were planned and designed in outline. Each of these sites failed to materialise for various reasons. Finally plans for the magnificent new site just outside Newmarket were approved and the practice moved in in 2008. The old High Street site is being developed for housing.

The new hospital is on a 15 acre site with 80 boxes and room for further expansion. In particular we have had room to build a special unit for scintigraphy and MRI scanning, an intensive care unit and isolation boxes.

Newmarket Equine Hospital.(Photo by the present author from his aeroplane).

Princess Haya at opening of hospital.

Chapter 6

They were giants in the days of old, You know

by: Sir Mark Prescott Bt

S ir Mark Prescott is the third Baronet. Both his father and grandfather were MP's. A varied education at several prep schools and Harrow was terminated early, and he joined Sid Kernick and Frank Cundell's stables, riding under National Hunt rules, with limited success for three seasons. A broken back, sustained at Wye Racecourse, necessitated a lengthy spell in hospital, after which he became Assistant Trainer to Jack Waugh in Newmarket for 2½ years. He took over from Mr Waugh, at Heath House in 1969, and has since trained almost 1,500 winners, including Group I performers Albanova, Alborada, Pivotal, Confidential Lady, Last Second and Hooray, as well as winning many of the big handicaps, such as the Cambridgeshire three times, and the Magnet Cup and Ebor twice.

Just before Christmas in 2010, Miss Mary Finch died - she was almost 80 and had worked, before her retirement in 1997, for 50 years as secretary to the oldest firm of vets in Newmarket, now known as The Newmarket Equine Hospital, but then based at Reynolds House in the High Street.

Petite, smart, neat and always immaculately turned out, with a carefully modulated voice, she embodied the iron hand in the velvet glove, and controlled every facet of office administration. A prodigious worker, as late as the 1970's, she was still doing all the accounts in longhand, and even those Leviathans of veterinary practice, the senior partners Fred Day and Bob Crowhurst, bowed to her organisational powers. Efficient, pedantic and a stickler for correctness and good manners, she was not without humour, but seldom allowed that side of her character to appear in public.

Back in the 70's, one freezing cold Christmas Eve, after evening stables -at about 6:30pm - I rang the office to report that we had a yearling with colic.

"Now Miss Finch, Sir Mark here; I suppose, whilst we're all still flogging away, all those vets of yours are sitting around eating mince pies and wearing their Father Christmas hats! Could you dig one of them out and get him up here as soon as possible, to give this yearling of mine a wash out with oil and salts?"

"Please hold on Sir Mark, I will see if I can find one of them, and will get him to come up straight away..." she trilled, before putting her hand over the receiver.

I could just hear her voice, indistinctly relaying my request, before her decorum slipped sufficiently for her hand to partially move from the mouthpiece,

"Well, really!" she said, her voice now rising and crystal clear *"Well really, this will never do; one of you will have to go up there!"* - and one duly came. No less than the great man himself, Mr Crowhurst.

In those days, we were only scratching the surface of today's veterinary knowledge, and blood tests were in their infancy. Results took three or four days to arrive by post, forwarded on from the analyst, via the vet's office.

Even Miss Finch was eventually proved to be fallible. On opening my post, prior to one of SHERGAR's big race appearances, instead of the blood result for one of my workaday horses, I found that Miss Finch had inadvertently sent me the full blood picture for the mighty Derby winner, trained by Mr M.R. (now Sir Michael) Stoute. Having read it once, I anonymously dropped off the offending result, in a clean envelope, to Michael's office. I then could not resist seizing the opportunity for some fun at poor Miss Finch's expense. I awaited the lunch time lull at the vet's office before ringing, Miss Finch, of course, never deserting her post for anything so unnecessary as lunch, picked up the phone.

"Now, Miss Finch, it's Sir Mark here. Are there any vets about?" "No Sir Mark, I'm afraid everyone is out of the office" she replied with typical diplomacy.

"Good. Just as well. Look, I want to thank you so much for sending me SHERGAR's blood result - priceless information. He can't win off that and it is really too good of you to give me this chance.

Before I get stuck into the bookmakers, I was just wondering what horse you wanted me to back for you against SHERGAR in the big race next weekend?"

"Ooh, no, no Sir Mark"

"Sshh, sshh Miss Finch. Don't protest, you don't have to explain to me, just let me know how much you want to put on, and which horse you fancy, and leave the rest to me."

I had goaded her into a frenzy of anxiety, before I put her out of her misery, by explaining that the result had been delivered safely to Beechurst Stables, in a plain envelope, and no-one would ever know of her unheard of mistake until the day she died - a day which so sadly came to pass in 2010.

My arrival in Newmarket concurred with the days when only one firm of vets serviced the whole horse population of Newmarket. At that time there were only 35 trainers in the town (most were related, three were Jarvises and four were Waughs) and there were less than 750 horses in training (as opposed to the 81 trainers and 2,650 horses of today).

Each of the senior partners, Fred Day and Bob Crowhurst, strode over their profession like a colossus. As an impressionable young man, it was their character that now dominates my recall, and it is easy to forget that each had attained their elevated position in the profession by being at the cutting edge of veterinary knowledge at the time.

Fred Day had pioneered the rectal examination of mares, which is now commonplace, whilst Bob Crowhurst, who, as a young man had spent some time in Kentucky, had led the way in colic surgery for foals, which, in the past, had merely been left to die.

A Newmarket man through and through, Fred Day was the older, and a direct link with bygone days, being a grandson of the Classic winning trainer of the same name (who was also a vet), and the son of Reg Day. Reg Day was still training in my time at Newmarket. He had ridden at the last National Hunt meeting run at Newmarket, on what is the Links today, and had first held a trainer's licence when he was only 17. He trained at Terrace House (now part of Tattersalls Sales complex), having charge of SWEET SOLERA, who won the 1961 1,000 Guineas and Oaks, when he had been a licence holder for 61 years and was aged 78.

Fred Day was a big man, but no horseman; a heavy smoker, a bon viveur and a crack shot in the shooting field, he had a liquid, deep, gravelly voice that the opposite sex found attractive. As a vet he was as proficient with horses in training as he was with animals at stud.

At that time, the concept of the horse as a working animal had not been completely lost, as was evinced by my first encounter with this essentially practical man.

I had only been with Mr Jack Waugh, as Assistant Trainer, for a matter of days, when a chestnut colt (out of the useful PANAMA HAT), owned by the late Lord Fairhaven, arrived to be broken. The colt's character was a combustible mixture, as he proved to be highly sexed, wilful and nervous.

Whilst being driven in long reins round the cinder track (which at that time circled the paddock at Heath House), the colt got into long strides, tucking his head in between his legs, and began to tow the lad behind him at increasing speed. The latter was either too weak or too incompetent to pull him round on one rein, in the prescribed manner in such circumstances. As a result, the animal took off round the paddock, and the pair gathered momentum with frightening rapidity. After being dragged an entire circuit, eventually the poor man, having been swung wider at each turn, had no option but to release his grip on the reins. With the loose long-reins now flapping behind him, the yearling was goaded on into a terrified, flat out gallop. No amount of waving arms, or cries of *"woah, woah, woah!"* from well meaning bystanders could either deflect, or break, his blind gallop. Having completed two circuits of the paddock, and thereby gaining maximum momentum, without his stride faltering, the horse then galloped head on into the surrounding flint wall with a dull but resounding thud. As the wall totally collapsed, a cloud of dust, like a small nuclear mushroom cloud, rose above his prostrate body - followed subsequently by an eerie silence.

Mr Waugh, who had been in the office, which looked out onto the yard, advanced across the paddock to inspect a scene of devastation - the wall demolished; the horse, perfectly still, was covered in flints and chalk. His eyes were rolled up into his head, his forehead and knees gashed open, and more worrying still, there was a steady stream of blood from both nostrils and the one, visible ear. There was only one consolation; his heart was still beating, as his jugular vein could be seen throbbing.

"Well, he's not dead then" observed the trainer, making, I thought, the very best of the situation, *"Go into the office, Boy, and ring for Mr Day."* Within 10 minutes, Mr Day arrived, carrying a Gladstone bag. In consultation with Mr Waugh, he examined the horse intently but silently, whilst I stood at its head. They then broke off into a huddle.

"I'd get on with it now" I heard Mr Waugh call out to Mr Day, as the latter went off to his car, to return shortly with another, larger bag of veterinary implements.

Anxious to impress my new employer (and at the same time display my understanding of such events), without awaiting instructions, I took the tack off the unconcious animal and then commenced to pull up the brow band of the bridle, to enable Mr Day to place, what I deemed to be the inevitable bullet, in its forehead.

"No, no" said Mr Day on his return, a touch of exasperation in his voice, *"What are you doing? We're going to geld him, for God's sake, not shoot him!"*

Shortly after this *al fresco* operation, the horse came round and, as the expression goes, found himself 'two stone lighter than before'. Subsequently he made a full recovery and, named SUN MAJOR, went on to win several races as a two-year-old in Britain, before becoming a near top flight performer in the Argentine.

Fred Day was one of my Governor Mr Waugh's greatest friends. After they had had a day's shooting together, I can still hear in my mind the peals of laughter that used to emanate from the sitting room at Heath House, as I beavered away in the adjacent office. Bay Parkinson and Owen Ambrose (both sporting Fen farmers and occasional racehorse owners) and Sam Thirlby (who, in Lincolnshire, grew most of our hay and drum-threshed straw) were their other usual companions.

Jack Waugh was a third generation Newmarket Trainer. He had had the misfortune to be at the first two fiascos of the Second World War - Dieppe and Dunkirk - he was wounded and invalided out of the army in 1942, and trained at Heath House until 1969. A noted disciplinarian, he was a first class stableman and conscientious to the extreme. His best horses were ARABIAN NIGHT (2nd in the Derby), MATADOR, OSTRRYA, FRENCH FERN, STAR MOSS (2nd in the St Leger) and LUCASLAND. He was also a first class shot and an exceptional gun dog trainer. He and Fred Day were childhood friends and had been at school together. As a result of their friendship, it was Fred Day who attended to the bulk of the veterinary work at Heath House. Technically he was immensely proficient and, to this day, I have never, before or since, seen anyone apply bandages to a horse's foot, knee or hock with a greater combination of speed, skill and dexterity.

He was a stickler for the lost art of stable management. No doubt this dated from the pre-antibiotic days, during which time he had assisted his father, when any minor wound, not attended to meticulously as soon as it was discovered, could precipitate a life-threatening infection - *"Who's supposed to have dressed this wound?"* he would say accusingly, whilst staring intently at Jack Button, Mr Waugh's head lad, and myself. *'The hair's not been clipped off properly around the cut"*, he would add, pointing to a gash sustained earlier in the day by a particularly sensitive and bitchy filly, to a particularly ticklish and awkward part of her anatomy, *"Get it done properly and I'll be back in 20 minutes,"* and, whilst Jack and I diced with death to carry out his instructions, he would head to the house for a cigarette, a fortifying drink and a chinwag with the Governor.

The same rules applied at Reynolds House. I recall having to visit a seriously sick horse at 2am one morning. Mr Day was as smart and trimmed as if it had been midday, but the yard girl looked tousled and had evidently been late. Mr Day was in full flow:
"It's no good you telling me how much you love these horses; and it's no good kissing them either; they don't give a bugger. All they care about is that you are on time and think about them all the time. I don't love them and I certainly don't kiss them, but they don't have to worry about me forgetting them either."

In his prime he was physically immensely strong, and it was an education to see him handle an obstreperous colt. With no sedatives available, a degree of strength, less essential today, was imperative then. *"Come here you saucy bugger, and don't think you can pull me about!"* he would say, seizing its headcollar and shaking its head until its teeth rattled.

As a result, he rightly prided himself in doing the mundane, but muscular task of teeth rasping -

a job today likely to be passed down to a less exalted member of the practice.

All horses in our stable had their teeth rasped four times a year, and Jack Button and I would have to have two buckets of warm, disinfected water at the ready - one for the rasps, the other for the teeth and caps which were to be extracted. At the appointed hour, the great man would advance down the yard, sleeves rolled up, a yellow towel in his pocket, to wipe away any blood or saliva, and a twitch swinging by his side. He was insistent that each horse's head be held at the appropriate angle. Not every horse was immediately compliant, and he would be sharply critical of any deficiency in this matter. *"Mark, are you going to hold its head straight or not?"* he would bark, pausing for a moment for effect, with his hands on his hips in exasperation. I would nod back meekly. *"Well get hold of it will you, or I'll have to show you how."*

There was however, one horse at that time which had defeated all prior efforts to rasp his teeth for the last four years. Therefore, as we worked our way down the line of the main yard stables, Jack Button and I judged it prudent to pass by his box.

"Woah" said Mr Day, *"You've missed one"*
"But that's NATIONAL TRUST" I ventured,
"no-one's done him yet, you tried last..........."
"Rubbish" he retorted *"and you two stay out of the way"* he added disdainfully, closing the box door behind him, catching hold of the horse's headcollar with one hand, and inserting the rasp into the corner of his mouth with the other.

As he made the first forward, thrusting movement with the rasp on its teeth, to our secret delight, the horse flung Mr Day round the box, so that he resembled the 'Daring Young Man on the Flying Trapeze', until, with the ease of a Highland games contestant throwing the hammer, it hurled the great veterinarian into the far corner of the box. It then galloped round the stable like a circus horse, all the while taking pot shots at its victim with its hind legs. Mr Day was forced to seek an undignified refuge beneath the water manger.

A voice from the back of the box called out:*"Mark, Jack, get hold of that bloody horse, will you? What are you doing outside the box anyway?"*

Once he had been rescued, we proceeded without comment to the next horse. *"Strange thing"* he confided, dusting down his cavalry twill trousers and keen to regain his reputation, *"that*

horse didn't have any sharp edges at all. No point in us doing him again, you know....!"

Fred Day retired from veterinary practice in 1972 to take up the position of Stud Manager to Lady Macdonald-Buchannan at the Lordship and Egerton Studs, and in 1979 he was awarded the OBE. Sadly, his latter years were not to be filled with contentment. Having nursed his first wife through a long illness, quite soon afterwards he married a local and glamorous merry widow, but the union was not a success. He sold his house and moved into hers, where he found himself permitted to smoke only in an outlying room. Shortly afterwards, he gradually fell into the ever tightening and relentless grip of Alzheimer's disease, and was forced to give up Stud Management. Thereafter he gradually retreated into his own, almost silent, world.

He was a sad relic when I visited him for the last time. Still smoking his beloved Senior Service cigarettes, he gazed vacantly through the window into the garden outside. His powerful frame and agile mind, were now so diminished that I was reminded of a once great vessel left to rot, unattended and almost forgotten, on the mud flats of a slow flowing estuary - and gradually the tide was going out.

"I'm sorry," he said *I cant think who are. You see I've got this awful disease....but.... I can't remember what it's called   "*

He died, rightly revered as a giant of his time, in 1995.

Bob Crowhurst was a similar, dominant character. He inspired love and affection as easily as hate and fear, but no-one ever doubted either his skill or his competence.

Dark, medium-sized and sharp featured, he walked purposefully, his toes turned out, with a slightly nautical gait, and had a penchant for speaking in short, clipped, staccato sentences that brooked no contradiction. He was born in 1913 in Maidstone, Kent, into a veterinary family. His father, grandfather, great grandfather and elder brother, Arnold, were all veterinary surgeons before him (as is his son, James, a Senior Partner in Newmarket Equine Hospital today). All were of a sporting bent.

He graduated from the Royal Veterinary College at the age of 21 and went straight to Newmarket, to work under Professor Brayley Reynolds. At the outbreak of the Second World War, he joined the Royal Army Veterinary Corps, and, in the winter of 1939/40, took a yeomanry division of cavalry with 11,000 horses to Palestine. He subsequently accompanied the Allies' ill-fated expedition to Greece in 1941 and, with six men, escaped capture by the Germans by sailing a small boat out of Crete, for which episode he was mentioned in dispatches.

During the Italian Campaign, he commanded veterinary hospitals at Persano and Bari, having in his care thousands of mules, which were used for transport in mountainous regions. Throughout the war he was accompanied by his batman, Jack Button, who was Jack Waugh's, and later my own, head lad. Bob Crowhurst ended the war as a Lieutenant Colonel and was awarded the OBE.

After the war, he rejoined the practice in Newmarket and was veterinary surgeon, on three occasions, to the British Olympic Show Jumping Team, for the Games held at Helsinki, Stockholm and Rome.

By the time I came to Newmarket, he was acknowledged to be the premier vet in the world for racehorse lameness, whose word was holy writ. In addition, he was racing manager to Lady Beaverbrook - thin, tall, elegant and seldom seen without dark glasses, she was renowned for her independent thought, spent lavishly at the sales, named all her horses with seven letters and suffered fools not at all. The partnership remained intact until Lady Beaverbrook's death, but their natural formality ensured that they never reached the stage of using first names to address one another.

Mr Crowhurst did little of the work at Heath House, and our paths did not really cross until the spring of my first season's training.

The understanding of respiratory disease in those days was limited in the extreme, and it was not unknown for horses to cough and display noses streaming with mucus for months on end. Many horses were steamed with Friar's Balsam, which smelt of eucalyptus and was poured into a bucket of steaming wood shavings. The horses' head was then covered in sacking, so that it could inhale the Vick-like vapours, which emanated from the bucket, whilst the shavings were being stirred manually. Onions were hung on the walls, and, at exercise, cough electuary, tied in women's tights, was wound round the bridle, using the cough lozenge principle, in an attempt to alleviate these symptoms.

By March of my first season, a couple of our two-year-olds had coughed consistently since early December, and had proved entirely resistant to a plethora of such homeopathic treatments. Mr Crowhurst was called in for advice.

In a time when few trainers commenced their profession until in their mid 30's, doubtless I was oversensitive to my lack of experience. Additionally, Mr Crowhurst did little to bolster my confidence, or disguise his contempt for someone with the effrontery to consider himself a trainer at the age of 21. He asked for details of the case history of the first horse.

"How long has it been coughing?"

"3-4 months, Sir."

"And what have you done in the meantime?"

"Left him in the box for several weeks, then resumed trotting and then cantering, and he has not improved or deteriorated one jot".

"And what treatments has he had?"

"Cough electuary, Friar's Balsam, onions in his box.... There's nothing else I can try."

"Well," he said *"what would you know about it anyway? You've only been at it five minutes."*

I felt the heat of indignant rage swell within me.

"Have you taken its temperature?" he queried; and then I heard myself saying slowly, through clenched teeth, *"I don't know, Mr Crowhurst. As you can imagine, I, of course, can't possibly read a thermometer - so, you'd better take it yourself!"* At which, he turned on his heel, walked out of the yard, leapt into his car, slammed the door, and disappeared in a hail of gravel. We never spoke again for ten years. And we both stuck to our guns.

A few years later he came up to Heath House to examine a horse for a private sale. Our petulance did neither of us credit, and we managed to conduct the whole operation through intermediaries, without speaking a word to one another - including observing the horse's wind test from opposite sides of the canter! The ice was eventually broken only when he was sent, by Miss Finch, to see the yearling with colic on Christmas Eve the following year.

Although, during the war they had fought their way together, through Palestine, Greece and Italy, their shared experiences had not resulted in any bond of affection being forged between Bob Crowhurst and his batman, my head lad, Jack Button.

On the few occasions that Mr Crowhurst came to Heath House, he did little to soften their former military relationship by standing at the stable gates and bellowing in a stentorian voice across the yard *"Button! Button! Button!"*

"Fuck him" Jack would say, whilst keeping walking, *"Fuck him. I could have shot him in the war you know, and nobody would have known!"*

One day, news reached Jack and me of an extraordinary occurrence at Mr Ian Walker's yard (Moulton Paddocks - now the home of Godolphin). A yearling, whilst being broken in, had been rollered for the first time late the preceding day. It had resented this vigorously. Quite correctly, once it had settled, it had been put back into its box and had been left overnight with the roller on, in order to accustom it to this new piece of equipment.

It was stabled in a cage box, with a passage outside. When the head lad went in to feed it on the following morning, the activity prompted it to have another attempt to shift the encumbrance. In so doing, whilst lashing out violently, it beat the head lad to the door. It galloped down the passage, all the while jumping and kicking, until its impetus took it scrambling up the stairs, at the end of the passage, and into the hay loft above.

Mr Crowhurst, we heard, had been called out to assist with the rescue -and we had immensely enjoyed imagining the scene.

All the more so, as Jack had informed me that, during the war, Mr Crowhurst, with Jack's assistance, and for strategic reasons, had hobdayed a vast number of mules and donkeys over a period of only a few days - the operation's side effect being that such animals, once they had been parachuted out of planes behind enemy lines, could not subsequently bray, and thus give away the allies position. The wretched animals duty done, on arrival at their final destination, they were then shot to prevent their falling into enemy hands.

Some days later, following the incident at Moulton Paddocks, whilst Mr Crowhurst was inspecting one of our horses, Jack and I executed our pre-prepared plan.

"I hear you had a bit of excitement up at Mr Walker's, Sir?" Jack ventured,

"Yes, yes. Horse in loft; horse sedated; Moons Plant Hire summoned; crane arrived; horse winched to safety - all in 60 minutes" came the reply, in typical rat-a-tat-tat fashion.

"Good Lord," I said, moving in for the kill, *"I'm surprised you took so long, Sir. I imagined you would have hobdayed it, tied a parachute on its back and shoved it out of the loft - and all in 30 minutes!"*

"That was war, for goodness sake. Button, what on earth have you been telling him?"

Unlike today's modern practitioners, it seemed at times that Mr Crowhurst's specialist subject was the lack of a bedside manner.

I had inherited, from Mr Waugh, the position of starter at the local Hunt's Point to Point, which in those days took place at Moulton Paddocks - a difficult track, up a steep hill one side and down the same steep hill the other. Our meeting was always one of the first of the season, and the over-keenness of the owner-riders of the time, coupled with the excessive exuberance and a lack of fitness of their mounts, frequently combined to cause a large number of the competitors to fail to complete the course.

At one particularly carnage-struck renewal, Mr Crowhurst, the Honorary Veterinary Surgeon at the meeting, passed my rostrum at a brisk walk. Like some genial, if rather sinister Pied Piper of Hamlyn, he was pursued by a string of wailing lady owners, each of whom was trailed by several sobbing infants. Blowing into his gun in a manner reminiscent of Wyatt Earp at the OK corral, Mr Crowhurst muttered to me out of the side of his mouth, as he passed by *"Bit of grief, what? Bit of grief. Can't make omelettes without breaking eggs, you know."*

As with so many strong characters, stories grew up around Mr Crowhurst, "when fact becomes legend, print the legend" is an old newspaper maxim. Mr Crowhurst, a keen hunting man, for a while, kept his hunter at the back of Reynolds House. During the hunting season, work permitting, he liked to go out once a week, generally on a Saturday, with the Newmarket & Thurlow hounds. Their country was mainly plough, with little to jump save the odd ditch, but which did afford excellent opportunities to view hounds at work.

His hunters were usually acquired locally, and normally gifted to him by grateful clients. During the year in question, however, his own hunter had gone wrong in mid-season, and a late substitute had had to be purchased, in haste, from a South Country dealer - *"Never had to buy one before you know - still, they tell me he has a fine pop in him"* was his comment.

One of the Junior Partners, tending to a sick horse, peered over the half door, and deferentially wished the Senior Partner a good day, as the new combination headed off for their first meet together. They made a grand spectacle - top hat and swallow tails, on a real good sort, part thoroughbred and well up to weight - and the pair trotted off up the High Street, full of anticipation, heading for the meet at Dullingham.

Surprisingly, for Mr Crowhurst was never one to miss out on an evening hunt, just after midday, a dejected pair could be viewed creeping stiffly back down the High Street. Mr Crowhurst, on foot, was hobbling beside his horse, his top hat now so flat that it resembled an old 78 rpm vinyl record, a lump of turf appeared to be lodged, or even growing, from the left side of his skull; he was soaked to the bone and covered in mud. His mount was lame, its bridle broken and tied with bailer twine, one ankle boot was missing and the other awry - evidently the Suffolk ditches had proved less suitable to the horse than the South Country fly fences, with which it had previously been familiar.

As they limped by, it was self evident that discretion should play the better part of valour and the junior vet felt it prudent to remain as invisible as possible. Further, without the need for lengthy deliberation, he decided against enquiring as to the success of the new combination's first venture together in the hunting field.

After a few minutes, a single shot rang out.

Moments later Mr Crowhurst dragged himself by the door, pausing only to confide that *"it was either him or me, you know. One of us had to go. Damned if it was going to be me...."*

Mr Crowhurst retired from the practice in 1985, and continued to run his small stud at Crockfords, which was situated opposite the back entrance to Tattersalls. In the latter days of his retirement, he became rather muddled, but touchingly, it was to Reynolds House that his homing instincts often took him, from whence Mrs Crowhurst would retrieve him in the car.

Although he died in 1995, his memory lives on, for he made an indelible impact on all that knew him. Only last year, a stud groom reminiscing about the vets he had known, recalled how Mr Crowhurst, on arrival at the stud, would sit in his car with his hand on the horn until someone came out to meet him, and yet, the stud groom became almost emotional when describing his admiration for the man, *"Now, Mr Crowhurst; he was a proper vet. If he had told me to stand on my head in the*

middle of that paddock for 20 minutes, I'd have done so, and what's more he'd have been right, and what's even more certain is that I'd have been pleased to do it!"

The retirements of Fred Day and Bob Crowhurst marked the end of an era that was already fast changing. The masculine world of the horseman vet, who diagnosed through experience and dictated by force of character, had given way to the march of science and the advent of female vets. Already in 1959, Dr Peter Rossdale, denied a partnership, had set up in opposition.

It is my experience that members of the veterinary profession are particularly prone to jealousy, and it was therefore no surprise to anyone that this schism, to the credit of no one, engendered such ill will and invective that a bitter taste was left to linger for many years.

Dr Rossdale had sought the advice of Professor Brayley Reynolds before making his move. Over a cup of tea, Professor Reynolds, the doyenne of his profession, opined to the young pretender *"Don't do it. It's been tried before. It won't work. I'd give you six months."*

Time has shown that it did work. The horse numbers grew, so that today both practices boast recently built, state of the art veterinary hospitals, and 100 vets and technicians service the needs of the horse population of Newmarket, that had required only 8 vets 50 years before.

The standard of care today is such that, when a horse of mine fell down on the roads, knocking askew two front teeth, he was treated within the hour, whilst the girl riding it, who had sustained similar injuries, waited three days before her teeth were even examined by a dentist.

I cannot suppose that such an order of priority would have sat easily with Mr Day and Mr Crowhurst. Undoubtedly, theirs was a robust approach to animal welfare. After all, though no fault of his, not one of the 11,000 horses sent off, under Mr Crowhurst's command, to Palestine during the war, was to survive. Theirs was an ethos founded on practicality, pragmatism, and both physical and mental strength. It was an ethos that had been shaped in the shadows and horrors of war (when the horse was a work animal) and that had yet to be tempered by today's significant scientific advances, or the spread of a anthropomorphism.

However, it remains undeniable that it is on the granite foundations, so uncompromisingly laid by

Fred Day and Bob Crowhurst, that both of today's veterinary centres of excellence in Newmarket have been built.

Mary Finch, as ever immaculate, receives the Thoroughbred Breeders Dominion award, in recognition of her 50 years service at Reynolds House, from the late Rt. Hon. Robin Cooke (the former Foreign Secretary) in 1999. The very personification of the iron hand in the velvet glove, as late as the 1970's Miss Finch was still doing all the practice accounts by hand, as well as organising the lives of all who worked in the ever expanding office.

Jack Button (head lad) on the left, with Jack Waugh (the trainer) on the right, in the paddock at Heath House in the late 1950's. Jack Button, who had been batman to Bob Crowhurst throughout the war, was head lad at Heath House from 1945-1972. In the background is the cinder track, covered with straw for the winter, and the flint wall that surrounded the yard at that time. Note the wooden water buckets, turned up in freezing conditions, and the top doors and windows closed - more importance being placed on warmth, as opposed to ventilation, at that period.

A photograph to delight any horseman, both horse and rider in complete harmony; Jack Button on LIGHT HARVEST. The horse was a very hard puller and winner of the Royal Hunt Cup (note the net on his noseband and the standing martingale). Jack's father had been a horse dealer, based in Luton, and Jack was a superb horseman - note his relaxed horse copers seat, his stick held half way up its length, and the soft hands. Also, in the background, notice the magnificent elm trees that lined the Bury Road in Newmarket, prior to falling victim to Dutch Elm disease 25 years ago.

COLOURS FLYING (MP), an ultimately disappointing brother to the top class ONCIDIUM, on the straw bed at Heath House, during the winter of 1968. Note the absence of a crash helmet, also the double leather reins with no rubber covering (a nightmare for riders, but still popular at the time) and the plastic shield on the horse's noseband, designed to deter the colt from rearing over backwards in the rain, as was his habit.

Two great figures of their time, Fred Day (right) with Noel (later Sir Noel) Murless, at the December Sales at Tattersalls, in 1957. Note the highly polished shoes and well pressed trousers, and the ever present Senior Service cigarette in the back of Fred Day's hand. Noel Murless, seldom seen without a cigarette or his pipe, was the leading trainer of his time, saddling 19 British Classic winners, in a career lasting from 1935 to 1976, when he handed over his Warren Place yard to his son-in-law, Henry Cecil, who took over his mantle. Sir Noel was knighted in 1972.

Fred Day, nearing retirement, in the paddocks at the Lordship & Egerton Studs, which at that time were both owned by Lady MacDonald-Buchannan and run in unison. Michael Oswald had previously left to manage the Royal Studs, to be followed at Lordship & Egerton, for a two year period, by Jack Waugh. The principal stallions standing there at that time were ABERNANT and MAJOR PORTION ROYAL PALACE and BRIGADIER GERARD joining the stallion roster shortly afterwards.

A cheery pair washing up after surgery at Reynolds House in the 1950's. On the left Bob Crowhurst and, on the right, his mentor Professor Brayley Reynolds, whose life had encompassed the change from horse-drawn power to the jet age. Born in Daventry, into a veterinary family, the youngest of 11 children, Brayley Reynolds commanded the Military Veterinary Hospital in Baghdad during the First World War, winning the OBE. He died in 1967, his mind and memory still as sharp as his surgeon's knife.

Bob Crowhurst has a merry wave for the photographer, as he leaves the Rutland Arms Hotel in Newmarket High Street, following a meet of the Newmarket and Thurlow foxhounds in the 1960's. For many years he was the Hunt's Chairman, a position occupied today by his son James. At his side is his daughter Charlotte (Char), who was to marry the well known and much lamented Bloodstock Agent, Joss Collins, for many years a lynch pin of the BBA.

David Ellis, who successfully bridged the gap between the old style practitioner and the modern age, joined the practice in 1967 and retired in 2009. A witness to the demise of Mr Crowhurst's new hunter, he specialised in bone surgery and the breeding side of the industry, and was the partner who designed, and saw through to its conclusion, the development of the Newmarket Equine Hospital.

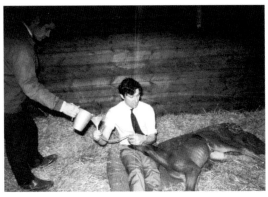

Peter Rossdale in 1962, at Cheveley Park Stud, nursing a sick foal. It was in the Dairy Yard at Cheveley Park that the new practice first performed operations. The association with Cheveley Park went back to 1948, when Peter and the stud's then owner, Albert Stafford-Smith, first shared ownership of a colt that Peter had bred on the Romney Marsh. Named PANTOMINE STAR, and gelded, it had the distinction of beating the subsequent Derby second, GAY TIME, in a nursery at Doncaster (albeit in receipt of over two stone).

The stable yard at Reynolds House, derelict today and awaiting development, the practice, now known as the Newmarket Equine Hospital, having moved to its state of the art site adjacent to the July Course roundabout. Note the walnut tree, frequently planted in racing stables, as the species was thought to ward off flies (viz, in Newmarket, Wroughton House, and a particularly fine example at what is now the Rous Memorial Cottages). To maintain tradition, five such trees have been planted on the new site.

Beaufort Cottage Stables, the first home of Rossdales. It was purchased in 1962 from Mr Lloyd of Rustons and Lloyd. Previously it was rented to Dick Perryman, who had trained CHAMOSSAIRE (St Leger 1945) and AIRBORNE (Derby & St Leger 1946) to win classics from the yard. It stands almost adjacent to the present King Edward VII Memorial Hall, which was built on the site of Lowther House Stables, from whence Fred Day's grandfather, Frederick William 'Bushranger' Day, had trained HANDICAPPER to win the 1901 2,000 Guineas for Sir Ernest Cassell.

And this is what it all came to - the Newmarket Equine Hospital, at the July course roundabout, opened by Princess Haya in 2009.

And this is what it all came to - Rossdales Equine Hospital and Diagnostic Centre, at Exning, opened by Her Majesty, The Queen. in 1998.

Chapter 7

The Beaufort Cottage Practice (Rossdale and Partners)

by: Sidney Ricketts LVO FRCPath FRCVS &
Nicholas Wingfield Digby BVSc MRCVS DL

Sidney Ricketts graduated from the University of Bristol in 1971, interned in equine medicine and surgery at the University of Pennsylvania, as a Thouron Fellow, before joining Rossdale & Partners, in 1972. He became a partner in the practice in 1975 and is now senior partner.

He was awarded a Fellowship of the Royal College of Veterinary Surgeons in 1978, a foundation Diploma in Equine Stud Medicine by the RCVS in 1986 and RCVS specialist status in Equine Stud Medicine, in 1991. The Queen bestowed on him the honour Lieutenant of the Royal Victorian Order (LVO) for services to the Royal Studs in 1998. He was awarded a Fellowship of the Royal College of Pathologists in 2004 and received an Honorary Membership of the British Equine Veterinary Association in 1997.

Nicholas Wingfield Digby was born in 1948 and brought up in Dorset. and graduated in 1972 from Bristol University Veterinary School. He then worked in the Department of Veterinary Surgery at Bristol before undertaking a year's clinical research funded by a Horserace Betting Levy Board Scholarship. Working with subfertile Thoroughbred mares and pony mare controls, a lifelong interest in equine reproduction developed resulting in publications on endometrial cytology and bacteriology. In 1973 he joined Rossdale and Partners. Released in 1975/76 to work for the Imperial Stables in Iran and Sykes and Partners in Sydney, Australia, he returned to Newmarket and became a partner in 1979 and has been Managing Partner since 2004. He is Chairman of the Trustees of Beaufort Cottage Educational Trust and a member of the scientific sub committee of the Horse Trust.

This contribution is intended to record the chronological development of the practice known now as Rossdale & Partners. Importantly, it also attempts to pay just tribute to the many veterinary surgeons, technical and lay staff upon whom the practice has depended for its existence and success.

The practice was started from Romney House on the Dullingham Road, Newmarket in 1959. Peter Rossdale had been an assistant to Reynolds and Partners for some 5 years, but a partnership offer was not forthcoming. To break away and set up a practice was, at the time, considered to be unethical but in the event was shown not to be illegal, as no contract existed between the individual employed and the employers. Peter was loyally supported by many local trainers, including, Paddy O'Gorman, Humphrey Cottrill, Neville Callaghan, John Winter, Bernard van Cutsem and Harry Wragg; by studfarm owners, Irving Allen of Derisley Wood Stud and the Stafford-Smiths of Cheveley Park Stud; and by owners Jack Gerber, breeder of Bebe Grande and Madame Arpad Plesch, the breeder of 3 international Derby winners including Psidium.

After having been a single-handed practitioner for two years, Peter was joined by Michael Hunt in 1961 and the practice moved to Beaufort Cottage Stables, High Street, Newmarket, which they leased and then bought from Mr Lloyd the solicitor. Michael had worked for John Burkhardt in equine practice in north Yorkshire and then as a houseman at the Equine Research Station. Initially, Peter and Michael shared the yard with Dick Perryman, who had trained Airborne to win the 1946 Derby from there. Peter and Michael were both sons of successful family doctors, who fully realised the importance of dedication and personal service to patients. This always-available, personal service to clients remains Rossdales & Partners' guiding ethos.

The history of the practice reflects the attitudes and *modus operandi* of the veterinary profession during these past 50 years. At its outset, claims of veterinary surgeons to be specialists was prohibited by the Royal College, even to the extent that to specify oneself as an equine practitioner was unallowable (see Chapter 2). Today, species and discipline specialisms are encouraged and awarded by RCVS certificates and diplomas. Following the award of diplomas and fellowships, the RCVS now recognises formal specialist status. The RCVS's stance towards specialism changed during the 1960s and 1970s, following public demand and aspirations for improved standards of veterinary care, demonstrated by the obvious benefits of developing specialisms in human health care. Many of the practice clinicians have subsequently achieved specialist recognition with the RCVS and European boards, in fields such as equine surgery, internal medicine and stud medicine.

The practice initially cared for horses and small animals but became entirely devoted to horses in the mid 1970s. The first move towards specialism was in surgery. Colin Peace joined the practice in 1965 and developed a surgical facility based upon those which he encountered during a visit to the USA and which were being developed at that time in Kentucky by specialist equine surgeons such as Robert Copelan. The facility included an operating table, which was part of the recovery floor of the room in which anaesthesia of the horse was induced and stabilised; and from which it recovered accordingly following surgery.

Of course, today as with all equine practices, facilities have advanced considerably and tribute is paid to Tim Greet, Richard Payne, Andy Bathe, Sarah Boys Smith and Lewis Smith in the context of the practice's surgical facilities and acumen. Raymond Hopes joined the practice in 1968, from horse practice in Reading where he worked with Alistair Fraser. He was the first to develop a horses-in-training speciality; and he also assisted Colin with anaesthesia.

Gathering of partners at the Jockey Club Rooms to celebrate the 50th anniversary of the practice.
l-r backrow: Ian Cameron, Marcus Head, Mike Shepherd, Andrew McGladdery, Ollie Pynn, Andy Bathe, Richard Payne, Fred Barrelet, Peter Ramzan.
l-r front row: Deidre Carson, Peter Rossdale, Colin Peace, Raymond Hopes, Michael Hunt, Sidney Ricketts, Tim Greet, Nick Wingfield Digby.

Members of staff (accounters, secretaries, technicians, nurses) who in 2011 had served more than 20 years in the practice.
l-r: Jenny Goodchild (37 years), Kath Gifkins (35), Tricia Burnip (23), Mary Ashpole (25), Brigitte Heard (24), John East (51), Helen Pringle (26), Kevin Grimes (32), Sally Green (27), Josie Meehan (22), Robert Cash (33).

One of the major interests of Peter and Michael was with what is termed the perinatal period, that is late pregnancy, birth and the newborn foal. This interest was encompassed within the important and widely practised criteria of equine reproduction, as established by Fred Day and others in the 1940s and 50s. The introduction of a speciality towards the newborn foal was unusual at the time and has been expanded and deepened over the 50 years of the practice by Sarah Stoneham, Nicky Holdstock and, more recently, by Celia Marr and Emily Haggett. This interest and expertise has culminated in the development of the specially designed Peter Rossdale Equine Foal Care Unit at the practice's equine hospital at Exning.

From 1979 to 2002, a herd of pony mares was maintained with successive funding by the Wellcome Trust and Horserace Betting Levy Board in order to study equine prematurity and similar conditions of the newborn foal. This concept was driven originally in co-operation with Leo Jeffcott, Twink Allen and Desmond Leadon. The herd was maintained first at the Equine Research Station, which became the Animal Health Trust, then at the Horserace Forensic Laboratory and finally at the Equine Fertility Unit. The first 5 years work was described in a paper published in the Veterinary Record[1] authored by Rossdale, Jeffcott and Leadon, which contained a list of 13 colleagues who participated up to that time. Jenny Ousey and Lorraine Palmer, who is currently a research co-ordinator in the practice, supervised the herd. The success of this venture clearly demonstrated that it was possible for clinicians in practice, in collaboration with others internationally, to conduct meaningful and well-acclaimed research, to the benefit of equine health and welfare.

The practice laboratory was first developed at the time the practice moved to Beaufort Cottage Stables in the mid-sixties. Haematological, biochemical, bacteriological and parasitological aids to diagnosis were usually performed at institute laboratories, such as the Equine Research Station. Data regarding normal and abnormal values were limited and samples collected in practice involved time delays and expense. The setting up of a practice laboratory appealed as a means of direct contribution to practical efficiency for diagnosing problems in the field and adding a service available at night, bank holidays and at weekends when appropriate.

The best example of specific laboratory measurements was the introduction of the capacity to measure arterial blood gas values by means of paO2, paCO2 and pH electrodes installed in the practice kitchen with essential help from Ian and Marian Silver from Cambridge University. The technique of arterial sample collection was learnt from Leslie Hall of the Cambridge Veterinary School and was particularly helpful for the diagnosis, treatment and management of the large number of maladjusted newborn foals that were seen at that time. These collaborations emphasise the developing relationships between practitioners and academics, a co-operation that is now firmly in place but, in the 1960s was rather rare.

The technician on whom the practice laboratory relied in its early days was Margaret Powney, sister of the Newmarket trainer, John Powney. In the early 1970s, Leo Mahaffey, an Australian who had been pathologist at the Equine Research Station, took over and developed the laboratory as both a practice aid, also providing a referral service to clients on a wider scale. On Leo's death, Sidney Ricketts developed what had become known as Beaufort Cottage Laboratories, in a wider and deeper aspect, helping form the now recognised speciality of equine clinical pathology. The laboratory has grown to become one of the largest and most internationally respected specialist equine pathology laboratories. With the technical skills of Robert Cash and Lorraine Palmer the new enzyme-linked immunosorbent assays (ELISA) and polymerase chain reaction (PCR) tests were more recently developed and incorporated with great success.

The laboratory now receives samples not only from Rossdale & Partners' clinicians but also from practices all over the UK and the EU. Sidney became a Fellow of the Royal College of Pathologists, probably unique for a career clinician in veterinary practice. This honour, awarded on the basis of his published works, followed his Fellowship of the RCVS for his thesis on endometrial biopsy in the mare, gained in 1978. In the laboratory, Sidney was joined by Annalisa Barrelet and, more recently Alastair Foote, a highly talented and enthusiastic young FRCPath, and Florence Gill.

The laboratory technical staff increased considerably in number over the years and mention must be made of those long serving members without whose support no laboratory can flourish. These include Kath Gifkins (35 years service), Robert Cash (33 years), Kevin Grimes (32 years) and Tricia Burnip (23 years). Mary Ashpole has been senior secretary to the laboratory for 25 years.

Within the development of specialisms, a division has developed over the years as between stud and stable practice. This was partly driven by client demands for dedication in respect of working time and knowledge of and expertise with developing specialist clinical procedures. Nick Wingfield Digby has been active in both of these areas with great success and, following Raymond's start, led the practice into recognising the division in terms of colleagues devoted entirely to one or the other. The stable side has grown with the recruitment of colleagues such as Neil Steven, who joined us from a practice in Epsom, then Michael Shepherd, Marcus Head, Graham Munroe, Rob Pilsworth, Peter Ramzan, Robert Dallas, Tim Hawthorne and Greg Sommerville. The studfarm side of the practice has been strengthened in addition to the present authors by Andrew McGladdery, Deidre Carson, Fred Barrelet, Ian Cameron, Oliver Pynn, Florence Gill and Philippa O'Brien.

Jack Sewell, a Sydney graduate who served in the practice during the 1970s. Returned to Australia and sadly died in 2004 from a car accident.

Colin Peace, following a family sabbatical, which consisted of a motoring expedition from Canada to Tierra del Fuego, decided to leave the practice and UK in 1980 and emigrated to Canada. Tim Greet joined from the Animal Health Trust and further developed the practice's surgical services and established a large clinical referral service from other veterinary surgeons in practices throughout UK and EU. Tim's specialist expertise is recognised internationally and he regularly lectures and operates abroad. Following Richard Payne's arrival in 1996 and the development of his surgical and managerial skills, Tim has assumed

important veterinary political roles, serving as president of the British Equine Veterinary Association (BEVA), the British Veterinary Association (BVA) and the World Equine Veterinary Association (WEVA).

Deidre Carson, an Australian graduate, joined the practice as a research graduate assistant and became a partner. She has contributed to many aspects of the practice's success and is currently President of BEVA. Fred Barrelet joined in 1991 and added a further dimension to the practice with his knowledge and expertise in performance horse work including 3-day eventing and endurance rides. He now has an important role with the Fédération Equestre Internationale (FEI). As a Swiss graduate, he provided an international dimension to the practice clientele and multi-linguistic skills. Andy Bathe, who was a surgical resident under Tim Greet, returned to the practice in 2003, bringing with him his internationally respected performance horse expertise and his innovative surgical skills. He now runs a very successful surgical residency programme at the practice's equine hospital and is partner-in-charge of the practice's equine diagnostic centre. Michael Sheppard, a New Zealander, has been official veterinary surgeon to the NZ Equestrian Team, recently succeeded at the 2010 Kentucky Equestrian Games by Oliver Pynn.

Imaging techniques, such as radiology, ultrasonography, magnetic resonance imaging (MRI), computerised tomography (CT) and digital radiography, together with scintigraphy, as with surgery, developed far beyond even the most forward-thinking practitioner in the 60's and 70's. The development of ultrasonography in the practice started in the 80's with the introduction of machines to scan the mare's uterus and ovaries, introduced by Eric Palmer in France and Twink Allen in Newmarket. Seeing is believing and all these technologies have become specialisms of today carried out with great effect in diagnosis, leading to prevention and cure of conditions, particularly of the abdomen and musculoskeletal systems.

Andrew McGladdery joined the practice in 1988 as an ultrasound imaging resident under Peter Rossdale and together they expanded the use of ultrasound scan diagnosis into non-reproductive internal medical fields. This has been further developed and progressed by Celia Marr. Rob Pilsworth made a significant contribution, particularly with bone scanning (scintigraphy) and has been followed by Sarah Powell, who, with Andy Bathe, Marcus Head, Sarah Boys Smith and Celia Marr, has developed the practice's MRI and CT imaging services to internationally respected levels. This team provides associated essential high-quality orthopaedic and medical diagnostic clinical capabilities.

Peter Ramzan, aided by Robert Dallas, has developed a well-respected equine dental speciality and is involved with the education and assessment of Equine Dental Technicians (EDTs).

Tim Greet and Richard Payne developed the practice's internship scheme, where enthusiastic young clinicians with one or 2 years of. experience in practice undergo three 6-month periods of rotation through the hospital and diagnostic centre, gaining invaluable skills and expertise, with expert supervision and exposure to a large case throughput. Some interns, following the completion of their 18-month period, have joined Sidney Ricketts for an additional stud season and have added equine stud medicine to their expertise, a field in which it is notably difficult to gain experience. The practice has enjoyed the presence of a number of excellent interns, some of whom have stayed on to become assistants and some who have become partners, including Michael Shepherd, Ian Cameron and Oliver Pynn. Others have moved on to great success in other leading UK equine practices and university veterinary schools internationally.

The importance of collaborative studies has been a tenet of the practice since its early days as expressed in an article in Equine Veterinary Journal, 1975, entitled in "Some reflections on clinical research"[2]. The abstract read, *"The place of clinical research in the veterinary profession is discussed against the author's personal experiences and in the context of how research workers, clinicians, teachers and veterinary students might be brought into a more cohesive unit through the development of a faculty of clinical research and experimental medicine. It is argued that students should receive training in research and teaching and that efforts should be made to break down the attitude of 'them' and 'us' which has traditionally tended to separate clinicians from academics".*

The academic, teaching and research interests of the practice are highlighted by the appointment to external professorships or visiting chairs for Sidney Ricketts at the University of Bristol and at the Royal Veterinary College and for Tim Greet and Celia Marr at Glasgow University. There have been in excess of 300 papers published in the scientific literature by various members of the practice over the past 50 years. Evidence-based medicine (EBM) has become a particular endeavour under the leadership of Celia Marr. The concept of EBM was first introduced in the substance of Peter Rossdale's Thesis for the Fellowship of the Royal College of Veterinary Surgeons entitled "A clinical and laboratory study of the health status of the newborn foal". Data collected was obtained during the course of practice work from sick and healthy cases and was subjected to statistical comparisons.

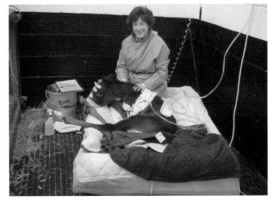

Sarah Stoneham in charge of a sick foal at the Exning Hospital.

Interest and success with collaborative research and publishing led to Peter Rossdale taking over the editorship of the Equine Veterinary Journal (EVJ) in 1979. His skills in this field, coupled with his amazing capacity for work and his capacity for leading and delegation, has largely resulted in EVJ now being recognised as one of the world's leading veterinary scientific journals. It is fitting that Peter has recently handed over the editor's baton to Celia Marr and he has been appointed emeritus editor.

As with all equine practices, the concept of 'hospitalisation' on a walk-in or longer-term basis has developed tremendously in scope over the past 50 years. In the early days, loose boxes and elementary means of confinement were the only ones available. However, as surgical, medical and foal intensive care became commonplace, so the quality of facilities necessarily improved and expanded. In 1991 the practice opened a diagnostic unit at Exning, just three miles from Newmarket, in association with the Exning Estates Company. The relationship with Simon Gibson and John East flourished and, in 1998, a new purpose-built equine surgical and medical hospital was added and opened by the Queen. In 2008, a new equine diagnostic centre, with state-of-the-art imaging facilities, was added and again opened by her Majesty.

Her Majesty The Queen at the opening of the hospital on April 23rd 1998.

Expertise is essential for the handling of horses in the hospital on and during walk-in procedures. Those involved have included trained nursing staff, such as long-serving Bony Millar and Josie Meehan, while long-serving yard personnel include Trina Stanbridge and Sue Myers.

No practice can exist without secretaries. In veterinary practice they not only act as the frontage between the clinicians and their clients but also fulfil a very significant role in the efficiency both of keeping records and recovering them at appropriate times. Susan Rogers (nee Apps) was the first secretary in the practice apart from Peter's wife Jill and Michael Hunt's wife Lorne. Jenny Ricketts was Peter's secretary until she married.

Lynda Searle joined the practice in the early 70s and left in the mid 80s. She presently resides in Australia but returns for 3 months of the year to run the sales office at Tattersalls for the practice. Brigitte Heard is now senior secretary in the practice and accompanied Peter on his rounds from 1987 to retirement in 2004. Jenny Goodchild, Mary Ashpole, Helen Pringle & Sally Green have served for very many years in accounts, laboratory and

the hospital, respectively. Sandy Ryan has become a highly successful head of the practice's export department and personal assistant to Nick Wingfield Digby.

The practice pharmacy, with its modern complexities, has developed to its current scope and efficiency largely through the work of Linda Galpin with the help of Sarah Stoneham and Deidre Carson.

Unfortunately, credit control is an ever more important part of the management of equine practice and Caroline Csaba runs a very pleasant and efficient team who do their best to help clients with financial difficulties.

Aerial view of practice hospital at Exning 2010.

Modern veterinary practices and their secretaries now need efficient computer systems to function efficiently. Sidney Ricketts was delegated partner-in-charge of practice finance, accounts and computerisation soon after he became a partner in 1975. In those days, IT systems were rudimentary to say the least, but with the help and support particularly of Jenny Goodchild in accounts, Mary Ashpole in the laboratory and Marcus Head, the practice's systems were developed to an extent that subsequently facilitated what was to become a highly successful relationship with Jeanne Razzell and Brian Whitt of Systems Support of Great Chesterford. This relationship has resulted in the development and continuing evolution of Rossdale & Partners' practice management IT system 'Eclipse', which now facilitates all aspects of daily work, from diaries to textual reports, from laboratory management and reports to digital imaging archive and retrieval, from pharmacy management to practice invoices, statements and case histories, all running within a 'need-to-know' password-protected security system. The practice's use of IT has been acknowledged by Apple who feature Rossdale & Partners on their business website. A very long 'journey' from the practice's pre-1975 hand written quarterly invoices!

The practice has a widely acclaimed website which provides a wealth of information of assistance to clients and referring veterinary surgeons and a Facebook page. This continually evolving project has been achieved by website designer Stephen Ricketts of Bojangles Design and editor Helen Gale, supervised by Sidney Ricketts, Fred Barrelet and Andy Bathe.

Veterinary practices do not manage themselves and the 50-year success story of Rossdale & Partners has required the partners to share the joys and challenges of making sure that day-to-day services work efficiently and well and that clients, partners and staff are fulfilled and content. Following Peter Rossdale's formation and highly successful early direction, the two present authors have enjoyed major responsibilities for the management of the practice. Deidre Carson provides an invaluable role with all aspects of what has become known as 'human resources'. Peter Stockbridge has become an invaluable member of the practice team as accountant and Nick Kelly as the hospital's administrator.

References

1.   Rossdale, P.D., Jeffcott, L.B. and Leadon, D.P. (1985) A collaborative project in veterinary practice: Developing a model of equine prematurity. Vet.Rec.117, 198-201.

2 .   Rossdale P.D. (1975) Reflections on clinical research Equine vet.J. 7, 81-85.

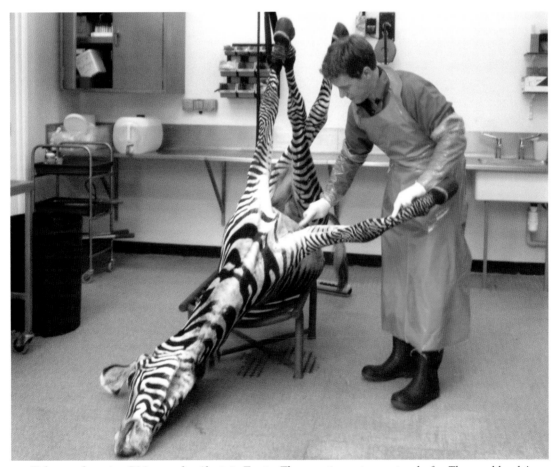

Zebra undergoing PM exam by Alastair Foote. The practice caters not only for Thoroughbreds!

Bacteriology laboratory with Kevin and Adam in attendance.

Tricia with instrument to measure hormones in blood and serum.

View of the section of Beaufort Cottage Laboratory where blood samples are analysed for cellular and biochemical constituents. Robert Cash and Michelle Haynes in attendance.

Robert standing next to instrument which is used to measure PCR (polymerase chain reaction). This is a technique which amplifies a piece of DNA across several orders of magnitude, thereby enabling identification of minute traces of bacteria and viruses in samples.

A third-generation multi-slice CT scanner was installed in 2008, allowing head and neck scans of adult horses to be performed on sedated standing horses and limb scans in anaesthetised horses. Whole body scans can be performed in young deeply sedated foals. Images can be manipulated to render 3-D reconstructions from 2-D slices (see page 16), producing not only exceptional images but also opening up new areas of diagnosis and treatment.

Hallmarq MRI system installed 2006 in Practice. This allows scans to be performed on the distal limb (including knee and hock) of sedated standing horses. MRI has greatly advanced diagnostic ability to more focussed treatments.

Chapter 8

The Animal Health Trust (AHT) and its Equine Research Station

by: Peter Webbon DVR PhD MRCVS

*P*eter qualified in 1971 from the Royal Veterinary College then, for three years, held a Horserace Betting Levy Board Research Training Scholarship. His PhD thesis was concerned with tendon injuries in horses. After several years in the clinical departments of the Royal Veterinary College, including directing the Large Animal Practice and Sefton Equine Hospital, he joined the Jockey Club staff in 1996 as its Chief Veterinary Adviser. He was appointed as Veterinary Director of the Jockey Club and then Chief Executive of the newly formed Horseracing Regulatory Authority. He took on the role of Chief Executive at the Animal Health Trust on 1st January 2007.

The history of the Animal Health Trust (AHT) and its Equine Research Station (ERS) provides a fascinating window through which to observe the development of the veterinary profession and, especially, the branch of it devoted to the care of horses.

The Veterinary Education Trust 1942

It would be unthinkable now to imagine that the British Veterinary Association could host a lunch, in a time of acute national crisis, that would be attended more or less willingly by many of the great and good of the land as well as eminent guests from the United States, Norway, Denmark, Belgium, Canada, and Australia among others. But, in September 1942, in spite of a journey to London that must have been difficult, at best, the overseas guests joined the Duke of Norfolk, the Minister of Agriculture, Viscounts Leverhulme and Bledisloe, Lords Horder and Stamp, Sir Weldon Dalrymple-Champneys and representatives of academic institutions and industry at the Mansion House to hear the President of the National Veterinary Medical Association (to become the BVA), Dr W R (Reg) Wooldridge, announce the formation of his brainchild, the Veterinary Education Trust with a plan to raise £1M to fund it.

After initial contributions from the Royal College of Veterinary Surgeons and the NVMA, the most rapid response to the call for funds came from the Thoroughbred Industry which, via a Bloodstock Industry Fund, launched and supported by Tattersalls in 1943, had raised £60,000 by

1951, a significant proportion of which came from the sale of donated stallion nominations.

The Wooldridge Vision

Wooldridge's original vision was that the Veterinary Education Trust would provide funds for undergraduate and post graduate education and to support research programmes. So, on the advice of his Scientific Advisory Committee, made up of Wooldridge, Professor William Miller and Dr John Hammond, together with two most eminent equine veterinary practitioners, Fred Day and Brayley Reynolds, two senior fellows were appointed; Dr J A Burkhardt to investigate heart problems in horses and W F Davidson to investigate infertility (both based at Cambridge). Miss Ann Russell was appointed as Bloodstock Research Scholar investigating red worm infestation at the Central Veterinary Laboratory, Weybridge.

The Equine Research Station (ERS)

Wooldridges's second ambition, of setting up research stations to study, and treat, the diseases of all domestic species moved closer in 1946 when Lady Yule put Balaton Lodge, in Newmarket, at the Trust's disposal for a nominal rent. This enabled the Equine Research Station to be opened in 1947 under the leadership of Professor Miller and the Veterinary Education Trust was renamed the Animal Health Trust (AHT) in 1948 to mark the change in emphasis of its activities. Balaton Lodge had seen service during the war as a military billet so Wooldridge and Miller had to carry out much of the necessary conversion and refurbishment through their own efforts. They were joined by Lt Col John Hickman, who was in charge of surgical work and who set a standard of excellence in orthopaedics that has been maintained by his successors until the present day.

Her Majesty the Queen visiting Balaton Lodge in 1955, four years before she became Patron of the Animal Health Trust.

Although the AHT subsequently opened a Canine Health Centre and Poultry and Livestock Research Stations, the remainder of this Chapter will be largely devoted to the ERS, its staff and its successes.

In a relatively short Chapter it is impossible to catalogue and describe the many veterinary and scientific landmarks that marked the development of the ERS. In trying to find a single word to describe them all, only one is wholly appropriate - novel. Over 65 years, to date, the ERS has made

contributions to horse welfare and to our understanding, prevention and treatment of equine disease on a scale and of an importance that I would challenge any other institution, anywhere in the world, to match.

The Educational and Research Remit

At its outset the ERS fulfilled its educational remit by putting on, in 1948 at the request of the Thoroughbred Breeders Association, the first ever course aimed at stud managers and employing the internal expertise of the Trust's staff, local veterinary expertise and the stud management team of the late 17th Earl of Derby.

The future of the ERS was made more secure in 1950 when, on the death of Lady Yule, her daughter Gladys gifted Balaton Lodge to the AHT. In the same year the Trust received what to some may be the ultimate sign of approval - regular mentions on the Archers! For others, the Trust featuring on the "Weeks Good Cause" on the Home Service, championed by Dirk Bogarde, would have been at least as memorable.

An aerial view of the Equine Research Station. The Gladys Yule surgical wing (bottom) and the Home of Rest boxes (middle) are on the right.

In 1955, the AHT started to produce a quarterly journal, "Animal Health" (that continued until 1976) "for those interested in farm livestock, horses and dogs". The first volume records a visit of HM the Queen to Balaton Lodge (the Queen was to become Patron in 1959) and gives an insight into the ERS activities at the time by listing the Departments that Her Majesty visited. These included parasitology, bacteriology, haematology, histology, forensic chemistry and the clinical departments where Her Majesty met Jim Roberts who was to revolutionise equine orthopaedic surgery. The cases seen by the Queen included 5 mares and their sick foals, three horses with heart abnormalities, and one cryptorchid. On seeing examples of tuberculous lesions in horses, Her Majesty questioned the wisdom of feeding unpasteurised cow's milk to supplement the diets of weaned foals.

Another insight into the early work of the ERS can be gained from the equine articles in "Animal Health" in the 1950s, which included;

Hydatid disease
Some problems of respiratory diseases
General problems of feeding
The Wobbler
The study of the blood
Epistaxis in racehorses
The "Barking" foal
Diarrhoea in the young foal
Care of the feet
Notes on twins in the mare

New Facilities

Her Majesty visited the ERS again in 1961 to open a new surgical suite which was widely acknowledged to set a new standard for equine surgical facilities and open the way to significant progress, especially in the surgical treatment of fractures. Although Mill Reef was, arguably, the most famous horse to be treated surgically by Jim Roberts, in 1972, when the horse suffered a condylar fracture on Ian Balding's Kingsclere gallops, in the early 1960s he performed a number of pioneering orthopaedic procedures on Thoroughbred racehorses, show jumpers and hunters.

While welcoming Her Majesty in 1961 the Duke of Norfolk was pleased to announce that Lord Rank had presented the Trust with Soham House, next door to Balaton Lodge, in memory of his brother J V Rank, a prominent racehorse owner. This gift was fortuitous because it coincided with the submission of the report of a Committee, chaired by the Duke of Norfolk, to respond to concerns that horses were being doped in races and the means that may be used to control this abuse. The report recommended the routine sampling of both winners and unplaced horses. The Animal Health Trust joined with the Jockey Club and the newly formed Horserace Betting Levy Board to open, in 1963, a forensic laboratory in Soham House and recruited Michael Moss, from the Metropolitan Police Laboratory at New Scotland Yard as its Head. The laboratory was to become the Horserace Forensic Laboratory and remained on the Soham House Site until 1997 when it moved to custom built new premises in Fordham, having long outgrown its original accommodation. Once open, the laboratories made it possible to embark on a programme of random and targeted post race testing which continues today. It is worth recalling that at the outset a trainer whose horse returned a positive sample automatically lost his (for women were not at the time allowed to train under Rules) licence.

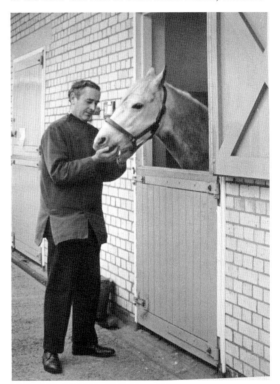

Jim Roberts with one of his patients.

Hill House

A famous episode occurred in 1967 when the well backed winner of the Schweppes Gold Trophy, Hill House, trained by Captain Ryan Price and ridden by Josh Gifford, was found to have abnormally high levels of cortisol in his post race urine sample. Reluctantly, the connections of the horse agreed that he could be transported to

69

Balaton Lodge for repeat sampling under the supervision of Michael Moss and Dr E G C Clarke (Royal Veterinary College) to determine whether the elevated cortisol level indicated an exogenous drug administration or was endogenous and normal for that horse. The latter view prevailed and, as a student at the Royal Veterinary College from 1966-1971, I was fascinated to hear Dr Clarke's lucid description of the investigation and its significance. Following the Hill House case, international racing authorities developed robust methods to agree thresholds for several endogenous substances and the Jockey Club changed its Rules so that horses could be ordered to be impounded so that abnormal levels of endogenous substances could be fully investigated.

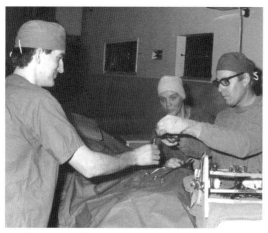

Bob Cook (right) hands a tissue specimen to Chris Colles.

Clinical Pathology:Leo Jeffcott refers later to the construction and opening, in 1969, of the new Clinical Pathology unit funded by a donation from Sir Michael Sobell, owner of the Derby winner Troy. The opening of the new post mortem facility followed closely on the recruitment of Katherine Whitwell to the Pathology Department. Over the next forty years, and continuing as I write, Katherine became the measure by which all other equine pathologists are judged. One of the most notable characteristics of the AHT in its first 65 years has been the way in which it has nurtured notable leading figures in the veterinary world who defined the organisation, were identified with it and either stayed on to produce outstanding work at the Trust or moved into the wider veterinary world to contribute to a general

elevation in veterinary standards. Katherine is a leading example of this and there are many more, three of whom Bob Cook, Leo Jeffcott and Tim Greet have contributed their own memories of their time at the ERS later in the Chapter. When the ERS was closed and all activities consolidated on the Lanwades site, the tradition of providing a first class pathology service was maintained with the construction of the Allen Centre, which provides the opportunity to conduct post mortem examinations on horses, which may have infectious diseases, within Category 3 containment.

Infectious Diseases

Royal Charter:By 1963, the year in which the Animal Health Trust was granted its Royal Charter, the ERS was arranged as six departments - pathology, parasitology, haematology, biochemistry, clinical medicine and surgery and continued to make diverse contributions to the equine veterinary profession. For example, in Pathology, the importance of venereal pathogens, especially Klebsiella was recognised after a disease outbreak. This led to a survey of cervical swabs from over 3,000 mares (from over 15% of which a pathogenic organism was detected) and the recommendation in 1966 by the Porchester Committee to the TBA that all mares should be swabbed before covering.

In 1965 many studs were affected by a virulent influenza outbreak. Recovered mares gave birth to foals that were temporarily protected by maternally derived immunity, but foals of unaffected mares were falling ill in the first few days of their lives, sometimes with fatal consequences. The Trust harvested serum from recovered mares and used it successfully to protect otherwise susceptible foals - there are records of over 160 foals treated in this way, none of which showed any signs of influenza.

In the same year the Horserace Betting Levy Board awarded the Trust a grant to construct a small interim virus research unit. However, most investigations into viral diseases of horses were conducted at Pirbright or the Royal Veterinary College until 1980 when, following the disastrous 1979 equine influenza epidemic, the Thoroughbred industry, led by Lord Porchester, funded the development of a virology unit at Balaton Lodge.

Dr. Mumford: Dr Jenny Mumford was recruited from the RVC to lead the project and the Unit was opened on March 16th 1981. Following the official opening by the Queen, Her Majesty hosted a luncheon at the Jockey Club Rooms attended by the President, the Duke of Norfolk, the Chairman of the Executive Committee, Lord Leverhulme and the AHT Director, Brian Singleton. Among the other guests was one of the AHT's rising stars, Tim Greet (see later for his personal memory of the day). Under Dr Mumford's guidance the virology unit went on to establish a pre-eminent position in the field of equine virology and benefitted from the formation in 1986 of the Equine Virology Research Foundation which aimed to raise £5,000,000 to study equine viral disease but, particularly, Equine Herpesvirus-1. Today the virology department remains one of the very few OIE reference laboratories for Equine Influenza and Equine Herpes Viruses across the world.

Working closely with the infectious disease scientists the ERS promoted epidemiology as an essential element in the investigation and control of disease outbreaks. Charles Frank and David (Dai) Powell, who was appointed on a special extra grant from the Horserace Betting Levy Board, led the way and James Wood and Richard Newton have contributed their special expertise. In conjunction, the virologists, bacteriologists and epidemiologists hold the thin line dividing the Thoroughbred racing and breeding industry from the ravages of infectious disease, where, in spite of increased awareness of the potential incursions of "exotic diseases" the most likely threat still comes from virulent forms of the endemic diseases that we deal with regularly - Influenza, Herpesvirus infections and Strangles.

The End of an Era

In January 1966 it was announced that the first Director of the ERS, Professor William Miller, was to retire, to be replaced by Richard Archer who was Head of the Station's Haematology Department. The founder of the AHT, Reg Wooldridge, became ill early in 1966 and in spite of making a good recovery, returning to work in April, he died suddenly in London on August 31st, aged 66.

The first Wooldridge Memorial Lecture was given at the 1967 BVA Congress by Wooldridge's close friend and collaborator, Professor Lord Stamp, where, having proposed that *"It is becoming evident that the future of medical and veterinary research lies more and more in the co-ordination of research activities and that old distinctions are largely irrelevant"*, he concluded his lecture by quoting Sir William Osler, who died in 1919, "There is only one medicine". Nearly a century after his death we still have not fully embraced the reality that mammalian medicine is a single entity with the human just one participating species and that comparative studies are likely to yield fundamental information more easily than those which are monospecific.

The founder, Reg Wooldridge (left), and Lord Rank on the occasion of the opening of the Forensic Laboratory in Soham House.

The 1980's signalled an interest in exercise physiology, led initially by David Snow who was at the ERS between 1983 and 1989 and developed by Roger Harris and David Marlin. Much of the early work was made possible by support from His Highness Sheikh Mohammed bin Rashid Al Maktoum. The highlight of the work of the Physiology Unit was the Atlanta project which ran from 1993 to 1996 and was initiated by concerns about the possible extreme conditions of high temperature and humidity which were likely to be encountered by horses competing in the 3-day event. The methods that were developed to cool horses, both during the speed and endurance phase, are now in routine use throughout the world in all horse sports.

Another area in which the AHT developed exceptional expertise was comparative ophthalmology, led by the inimitable Keith Barnett. Such was his expertise in eye diseases of all species, including the horse, that for many years he acted as a consultant to one of the two main Newmarket equine practices. His inspirational leadership has left a legacy of ophthalmological expertise at the Trust, with most of the experts equally at home with horses and small animals. David Donaldson now leads the equine ophthalmology team and already is making his mark in a discipline in which there remains great potential for progress.

Blood typing: As early as 1968 "Animal Health" carried an article on the application of blood typing studies, two of which were the definitive identification of individuals and verification of their parentage by excluding possible stallions or mares (unlikely). Messrs Weatherbys supported this work and started blood typing individual horses in 1972. In 1983 7,000 animals were blood typed and in 1986 only horses that had been blood typed at the ERS or Irish Equine Centre were eligible for entry into the General Stud Book. Mike Scott, Head of the Department of Immunogenetics was responsible for the blood typing both at the ERS and at the Irish Equine Centre. Blood typing has now been replaced by the use of genetic markers, but all foals registered in Britain are still typed at the Animal Health Trust by a team led by John Haslam.

Genetics: Arguably, the area in which the greatest progress has been made in the last decade has been genetics. Several geneticists have contributed to this, but credit for much of it must go to Matthew Binns and the collaboration that he developed with Twink Allen at the Equine Fertility Unit. One of the factors that contributed to the expansion of knowledge about equine genetics was the establishment of three horse reference families one of which, comprised of 3 generation full-siblings, was the result of the collaboration between the Animal Health Trust and the Equine Fertility Unit. AHT geneticists have been regular contributors to Havemeyer Equine Genetics

Workshops, which the Trust hosted in 2010. It was at the 6th Dorothy Russell Havemeyer Foundation International Equine Genome Mapping Workshop in Dublin in 2005 that the International Equine Genome Sequencing Consortium was conceived, which went on to collaborate with the Broad Institute to produce the first iteration of the equine genome in 2007, constructed using DNA from a Thoroughbred mare, Twilight. Very recently, in November 2009, a more detailed, high quality draft assembly was published with June Swinburne and Mark Vaudin from the AHT Genetics Department as two of the co-authors.

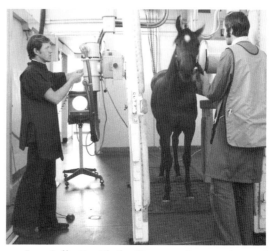

Leo Jeffcott with the X-ray equipment donated by Lady Beaverbrook.

Offices and stations: At one stage in its existence the Animal Health Trust had a Head Office in central London, a Livestock Research Center at Stock in Essex, a Poultry Research Station at Houghton Grange near Huntingdon, a Canine Health Centre at Lanwades Park near Newmarket, in addition to the Equine Research Station at Balaton Lodge. The Livestock Research Station was closed in 1971 due to lack of support. The Poultry Research Station was financed jointly by the Agricultural Research Council and was closed on the Houghton site in the mid 1980s by which time, as a consequence of the report in 1977 of a Committee set up by Lord Leverhulme, the London office had been closed and the administrative offices moved to Lanwades Park. Concurrent with the move from London, the decision was taken to create a post of Director of the Animal Health Trust to be responsible for all of its activities. Brian Singleton was appointed to this position so, in effect, the ERS only had two Directors in its own right from 1947 to 1977 - William Miller and Richard Archer.

The consolidation meant that the AHT was on just two sites and it was, therefore, only a matter of time until Balaton Lodge was closed and all of its activities moved to Lanwades Park. The laboratories took over the old Small Animal Centre and the clinical and research departments moved into a new Centre for Equine Studies. While the Centre originally housed equine clinical orthopaedics and research, together with cardiopulmonary medicine and research it now concentrates on orthopaedics and ophthalmology. Led by Sue Dyson who, over 30 years has advanced our understanding of orthopaedic conditions in horse through a staggering collection of publications and presentations, CES has pioneered the use of advanced imaging techniques including ultrasonography, scintigraphy and MRI which, as a result, are now routinely in use in many equine clinics in the UK and internationally.

I took over the role of Chief Executive of the Animal Health Trust in January 2007. It is an exciting, but challenging position. Challenging, not least, because of the formidable list of contributions that the Trust has made to the veterinary world since 1942 and because of the aura of those who have preceded me, particularly the original founder, Reg Wooldridge. I have the dual responsibilities of providing the funds, facilities and equipment to facilitate the work of our veterinarians and scientists while, at the same time, trying to ensure that the impact of their work is comparable to that of their predecessors. Only time will tell if I succeed. In the meantime it is a pleasure to conclude with the personal memories of three leaders in their own fields, whose careers owe (I know they would agree) much to the ERS, in the same way that the ERS owes much to them.

Bob Cook Writes:

April Fool's Day, 1969, was day one of my 8 years at the ERS . The focus of my research, then as now, was the head, neck and chest of the horse. Herewith a sketch of this segment of veterinary medicine in the 70s from Balaton Lodge, where the ERS was then located. Let the biopsy begin.

The endoscope I used from 1969-2003 was the same as the one I had used since 1960; a one meter, metal barrel, carrying glass optics and a terminal bulb powered by a 4.5 volt battery. It was, rather grandly, called a rhinolaryngoscope ('rhino' = nose; larynx = voice box). Under a new name, it was essentially the same instrument as originally developed for inspecting gun barrels. As a borescope, it was safe enough for the operator, the instrument and the gun but not when used for examining the throat of a fully conscious horse. No equine sedatives were available in those days, so the 'gun' was loaded. The likely impact of the vulcanite eyepiece on the operator's eye could be

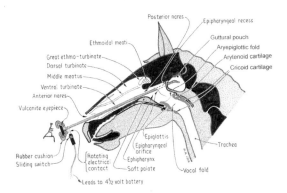

Normal anatomy and 70s style guttural pouch endoscopy. The red area shows the fungal mat of guttural pouch mycosis.
Colour key: black = bone; yellow = soft tissue; green = cartilage.

softened with a wrap of sponge rubber. The throat was seen *'as through a glass darkly.'* The number of veterinarians, worldwide, that had used such an instrument could be counted on one hand with several fingers missing. By trial and error, I learned how to get this device into the back of a horse's throat without bending the horse, the instrument or myself. To examine the guttural pouch meant passing it up to its hilt and requiring the horse to be a 'sword-swallower'. Curiosity overcame temerity and much was learned. Endoscopy became as indispensable for the diagnosis of diseases of the equine ear, nose and throat, as a hoof knife for the diagnosis of lameness.

When flexible fiberscopes became available (PW note: the first flexible endoscope was purchased by the ERS in 1973), the human oesophagoscope served as an equine laryngoscope. The flexibility made it safer for the patient and veterinarian. It was also more 'democratic' as equine endoscopy was no longer the preserve of a foolhardy few. The vastly improved lighting permitted photography. In the early days, if I wanted to illustrate what I was seeing, I had to paint a watercolour. Since the 70s, endoscopy has advanced technically and anatomically. The lung can now be 'scoped as well as the stomach. Video endoscopy of the standing horse has been followed by treadmill endoscopy and, most recently, by dynamic endoscopy - examination of the throat of a ridden horse at the gallop. This is not the equivalent of seeing the moons of Jupiter but it is a new world for equine veterinary medicine. "Nature composes some of her loveliest poems for the microscope and telescope," wrote Theodore Rozsak. Today he might have included the endoscope.

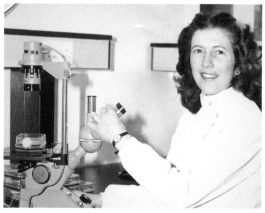

Jenny Mumford shortly after the virology unit was opened in 1981.

Back in the age of the borescope, I had described a fungal disease of the horse's Eustachian tube. One of the clinical signs of this 'new' disease (guttural pouch mycosis) was nose bleeding. Ferocious and sometimes fatal haemorrhages occurred from aneurysms on the internal carotid artery. At the ERS, with the help of Dr. D. Hawkins, a medical radiologist from Cambridge, we developed a radiographic technique for identifying these aneurysms. The damaged artery was then ligated before the horse bled to death.

Looking back, it is a surprise to be reminded that the chronic coughing horse used to be a clinical puzzle. The puzzle resolved into either 'dust or donkeys.' Maurice Round at the ERS had recently shown us that the donkey is an asymptomatic host for the equine lungworm. Horses grazing the same pastures often developed parasitic bronchitis. But stable dust was a much more common cause of 'broken wind' as it was of guttural pouch mycosis. Horses should not be housed in barns that double as storage facilities for slowly decaying vegetation - hay and straw.

In the 70s, I had the opportunity to examine many racehorses suffering from what at the time was referred to as 'broken blood vessels.' No one had asked which vessels it were that 'broke.' They were assumed to be in the nose and, accordingly, the condition was called epistaxis. The borescope enabled me to rule out the head as the source of the blood and conclude that these horses were bleeding from the lungs. John Pascoe in Australia confirmed this in 1981 by fiberscope surveys, naming the problem 'exercise-induced pulmonary haemorrhage' (EIPH). Subsequent surveys indicated that EIPH affects over 95% of Thoroughbred racehorses. This sounds like a harsh judgment on the Thoroughbred and a new slant on the 'blood' horse - when they run they bleed. But in fairness, the problem is not restricted to the Thoroughbred. It occurs in many other breeds and occupations, whenever the airway is obstructed. EIPH in the horse is analogous, in my opinion, to negative pressure pulmonary edema in man.

In 1969, the radiography facilities at the ERS were unremarkable but subsequently became outstanding. Bob Crowhurst in Newmarket, the veterinary advisor to Lady Beaverbrook, referred one of her horses from Major Hern's yard at Lambourn. Sea Epic, her favorite horse, *'swallowed its tongue.'* I wish I had known then what I now know about the cause of soft palate problems but, in the event, I operated on the horse and resected a small portion of its soft palate (staphylectomy). I 'phoned Lady Beaverbrook at 9.00 am prompt, each morning, so that she could receive a bulletin on her horse while she was having breakfast in bed. When her horse was discharged, she mentioned that she would like to give us something. Several months later, we heard from Bob Crowhurst, that Lady Beaverbrook wanted us to tell her what we would like. We had no idea what size gift she had in mind, so we originally suggested some quite modest piece of equipment. I don't know what was proposed at first or even, with tongue in cheek, on the second occasion but it was not enough. "No' she said, "I want to give you a real present." So now, with some trepidation, it was proposed that Lady Beaverbrook might like to give us a Siemens radiography unit, complete with fluoroscopy and tomography. This she did and the generous gift enabled us to overcome many barriers to diagnosis. Trying to cure a disease without knowledge of its cause is like sailing the Atlantic without a navigator. Dorsal displacement of the soft palate (DDSP) is a common source of asphyxia in the racehorse. Thanks to fluoroscopy and a study of Wood's comparative anatomy of the mammalian throat, I had learned a little about the problem but not the cause - this 'bit' came later.

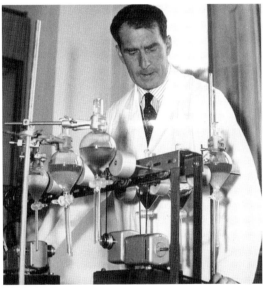

Michael Moss inspecting the tools of his forensic trade.

At the ERS, as during my previous years at the Glasgow Veterinary School and the Royal Veterinary College, I continued to encounter horses that suffered from the headshaking syndrome. This all too familiar problem was the bane of the horse, owner, and veterinarian, as the syndrome was notoriously recalcitrant to treatment. For a dressage horse, in particular, it was often career ending. The recurring reason for our inability to cure was, of course, that we did not understand the cause. Soon after I left Newmarket, I published four articles which, for the first time, described the syndrome and its investigation. Yet, in spite of spilling so much ink, I concluded the

series by admitting that I did not know the cause and could offer no treatment. Years later, I published another article, still with the same conclusion. Late in my career, I have realized that the bit is the most common cause of headshaking, DDSP and EIPH. The underlying reason for the head tossing spasms and other signs of facial pain is trigeminal neuralgia (tic douloureux). Nerve pain in the major sensory nerve to the head is, I conclude, triggered by the relentless and repetitive pressure of the bit on tongue, bone and teeth. In the 70s, in order to investigate these cases, I used to carry out a whole range of tests, mostly with unconvincing results. Similarly, I used to recommend a barrage of mostly ineffective 'treatments.' Life is simpler now, less expensive and more rewarding for all concerned. The first and most important step I recommend is removal of the bit. With this simple step, the majority of headshakers recover.

Richard Archer, who was Director of the ERS during my time there, encouraged me to study for a PhD and arranged for me to be admitted at his college, Trinity Hall. Kenneth Wilsdon, the senior Ear Nose and Throat consultant at Addenbrookes Hospital in Cambridge volunteered to be my supervisor for a study of recurrent laryngeal neuropathy (RLN) in the horse. He was most conscientious about his duties and would call in at Balaton Lodge for a chat every Thursday afternoon, after he had finished his clinic at the Newmarket Hospital. If I had to tackle some unfamiliar surgery, such as the repair of a cleft soft palate, I could appeal to him for support and he would scrub up with me. As Kenneth was deaf and dependent on lip reading, we communicated during these surgical duets by hand signals as we were both wearing masks. The tale has already been told of how my thesis travelled on the luggage rack of a carriage on the London-Edinburgh line for three months without being disturbed.

The same reference described the serendipitous discovery at the ERS of a spinal reflex in the horse. By slapping a horse on the left saddle patch, the right side of the voice box gives an answering twitch and vice-versa. I called it the thoraco-laryngeal reflex and subsequently developed a computer-based instrument that measured the response time from slap to twitch. A healthy nerve pathway allowed the signal to reach its destination faster than a diseased one. As a quantitative test for RLN it has merit but needs waveform analysis of the data to bring it to fruition. I hope that some researcher in the future will team up with a mathematician to complete this project. The same reflex proved valuable for the investigation of 'Wobblers' and other diseases of the spinal cord.

Equine dentistry in the 70s was not a speciality that had been widely adopted. Dentistry in practice consisted mainly of rasping teeth and removing temporary premolar caps. Dental cases referred to the ERS mostly involved congenital defects of the jaw or sinus infections that required removal of an upper molar tooth. Since then, much work has been accomplished in dental care for the horse, with many new problems being identified. Concurrently, the natural horsemanship movement has blossomed and many horses, in order to go barefoot, are now kept out of stables. A bonus of this more natural management of the horse will, I predict, be a decrease in dental problems. Museum surveys have shown me that the oral health of wild horses is excellent. They can do just fine without dentists, as they can without farriers and veterinarians. This in marked contrast to 66 museum skulls from domestic horses in which not less than 88% showed evidence of bit damage to the teeth or the bars of the mouth.

I am obliged to conclude that the main cause of disease in the front end of the horse is *Homo sapiens*.

Leo Jeffcott Writes:

ERS 1967-1972 - the scene in Pathology My early days at the ERS (ERS) were very exciting; I arrived at Balaton Lodge as a brand new graduate from the Royal Veterinary College on 4 January 1967 to my first job in the profession - Assistant Pathologist. The only equine job I could find, as opportunities particularly in Newmarket were pretty scarce in those days. I had decided it would be good to begin by being able to cut them up and understand basic pathology before becoming a clinician which I eventually did 5 years later in 1972.

The Director of the ERS at this time was Professor Willie Miller, and he was on the point of retirement in early '67. He duly introduced me to my boss, Dr Leo Mahaffey, the Senior Pathologist. Leo was a fascinating Australian who seemed to know everything there was to know about horses,

pathology and racing. From the start I found the work fascinating with plenty of stillbirths, abortions and neonatal foals to the post mortem room that breeding season. The facilities were not great - we worked on an old concrete slab in a converted garage next to the thatched stables (known as the 'black boxes'. However, the laboratories were housed in the main training yard of Balaton Lodge, and while not state-of-the-art were easily capable of providing all the diagnostic support required. There was also an excellent team of laboratory technicians, lead by Jenny Short in bacteriology, Carol Warren (Big Carol, as she was affectionately called) in histology, Penny Close in haematology and Dave Elton in clinical pathology.

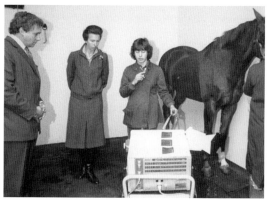

Sue Dyson explains an ultrasound image to Andrew Higgins and the Princess Royal.

Technical assistance in the pm room was provided by Pat Nelson whose real profession was a stable lad - what he lacked in technical ability he made up for in enthusiasm, and we got on very well. I learnt how to examine a foetus for contagious abortion, EHV (herpesvirus or rhinopneumonitis virus) from Leo Mahaffey and from Jim Atherton, the Senior Technician, to make a preliminary diagnosis by cutting frozen sections of liver and looking for typical lesions with characteristic inclusion bodies. Material was then sent off to Bob Burrows at Pirbright for confirmation by virus isolation. Fortunately, we only had a few isolated cases in the 1967 season with no major outbreaks to upset the breeding industry.

Within a few weeks of my starting Leo Mahaffey left the ERS to set up the Beaufort Cottage Laboratory in Peter Rossdale's practice, which after 45 years is still highly successful and run by Sidney Ricketts. The new Senior

Pathologist to be appointed was Dr Hugh Platt from Pirbright, but he didn't start until later in the summer. So much of the time I was left to my own devices, and the Day and Crowhurst practice at March House kept me very busy. However, in March '67 the new Director of the ERS, Dr Richard Archer, the esteemed haematologist and eosinophil 'king', invited the most highly regarded equine pathologist in the States, Professor Jim Rooney, to come for a six month sabbatical at the ERS. This renowned, but controversial, pathologist was from the Department of Veterinary Science, University of Kentucky in Lexington in the middle of the most important breeding area in the States where they carried out >1000 post mortems a year. For a young pathologist this was a great opportunity to learn from the "master". I became an expert on the Rooney technique for equine post mortems, and gradually Pat Nelson and I were able to keep up with the speed that Jim managed to work at for each autopsy. It was painstakingly thorough with every organ, joint, the head, brain and even the cervical spine and cord examined in detail. His skill and breadth of knowledge of pathology of the cervical and thoracolumbar spine set me on a 40 year path to try and learn more about backs and wobblers.

Jim's main purpose in coming to Newmarket and the ERS was to complete his first major book, The Biomechanics of Lameness in Horses, but he found time to assist with much of the routine pathology coming into the ERS, present papers at BEVA meetings and Congress and write a number of papers, including one with me! I always kept in touch with Jim until his death a few years ago - he was a remarkable man who made an enormous contribution to equine pathology through his work, books and publications.

In August '67 Hugh Platt arrived and started his work on his perinatal mortality survey. His broad experience in research, histopathology and general pathology was very welcome, and it meant that I didn't have to be on duty 100% of the time! It also gave me a chance to begin a PhD as an external candidate in the University of London. This was a 4 year program and involved an investigation into the mechanism of transfer of passive immunity from the mare to the newly born foal. Whilst the importance of passive immunity was clearly recognised on the studs, the complex mechanism of how immunoglobulins reached the foal's circulation after birth was not known, and more

importantly how efficient it was and how long it could function after birth. The project took 4 years and involved monitoring the parturition and perinatal period of 24 pony mares over 3 breeding seasons to identify the fascinating process of pinocytosis of macromolecules by the small intestinal villi, and transfer to the lymphatics before finally reaching the systemic circulation.

The other big event that happened in Pathology in late '68 was the appointment of a third pathologist at the ERS. Katherine Whitwell was a Liverpool graduate who had been working in practice with Terry Boundy in Wales before coming to Balaton. She has been there one way or another ever since, and has made a contribution to equine pathology that is second to none. Her work on placentation, wobbler disease, grass sickness and the involvement of hares, and many other themes has made an important impact through her publications.

My final involvement with pathology at the ERS was with the building and opening of the Michael Sobell Post Mortem Room. For many this was just a strange, large, very tall structure with terrazzo benches, Rooney-type exam tables and a heavy duty band saw, but for me it was 'heaven' to be able to carry out detailed post mortem examinations on valuable horses referred from practice. Between the three of us many thousands of post mortems must have been undertaken until the Pathology Department moved out to Lanwades Park.

The opening of the Michael Sobell Unit was carried out in late 1969, and was a very special day for the ERS and the small Pathology team. Richard Archer staged an impressive event with many VIP's from racing and breeding. My new wife, Tisza (also a member of staff in Clinical Pathology) was chosen to present the ceremonial scissors to Michael Sobell to carry out the official opening of the building. It was state-of-the-art at the time and money well spent as many hundreds of publications came directly from the work undertaken there.

Since those early days, much has come out of equine pathology at the Animal Health Trust. The great majority of this is due to the many accomplishments of Katherine Whitwell. Her broad clinical knowledge, meticulous attention to detail and ability to think laterally has been a boon to practitioners, horse owners and studs for over 40 years. I completed my PhD in February 1972 which coincided with the birth of my first daughter,

Julie Marie. After that I was moved to the Clinical Department and was given the responsibility of running the new x-ray equipment so kindly donated by funds from Lady Beaverbrook. My stint in pathology at the ERS was the foundation of my clinical career in diagnostic imaging, orthopaedics and problems of the vertebral column.

The following figures are taken from my PhD thesis *"Perinatal studies in equidae with special reference to passive transfer of immunity"*, University of London, 1972.

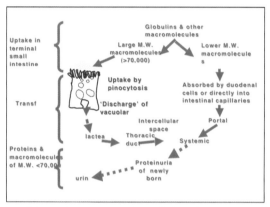

Schematic representation of the absorption of immunoglobulins and other macromolecules from the small intestine of the horse.

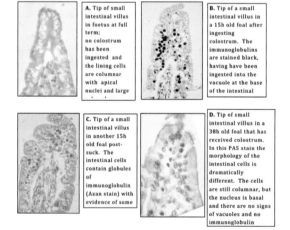

Some histological observations of the specialised cells lining to small intestine that are capable of absorbing macromolecules in the first 24 hours of life.

Tim Greet Writes:

The Animal Health Trust in the 1970s- my introduction to Newmarket.

I graduated from the University of Glasgow in the summer of 1976 and undertook a study for a Master's degree in the surgery department of the veterinary school immediately afterwards. I was very fortunate in having been awarded a three-year scholarship by the Horserace Betting Levy Board to study diseases of the ear, nose and throat, with particular reference to the horse. During my first year of study at the suggestion of the Levy Board, I visited the Animal Health Trust in Newmarket. In those days the unit dealing with horses was called the ERS, situated in Snailwell Road in a former racing yard called Balaton Lodge.

The reason for my visit was the internationally recognised respiratory clinician, Bob Cook. He had more or less single-handedly developed the specialism of equine ear, nose and throat disease, and at my Levy Board interview some surprise had been expressed at my intention to study in Glasgow and not Newmarket.

I spent almost a week during the Easter of 1977 at the ERS, which at that time employed three veterinary surgeons in its clinical department; Cook, Leo Jeffcott and Chris Colles. Jeffcott, having originally gained a PhD in the pathology department, was developing a special interest in the equine back and pelvis. The AHT had recently acquired a high-powered x-ray generator at a time when such equipment was very rare in the veterinary world; this allowed radiological assessment of these more radiodense areas of the horse for the first time. Jeffcott was thus able to correlate the clinical and radiological features of problems affecting the back, pelvis and proximal limb. Colles was employed as anaesthetist and like his predecessor, Colonel Langley, he had taken an interest in foot lameness. He was developing a theory about navicular disease, which received much attention at the time but has subsequently fallen into disfavour.

I was welcomed warmly at Balaton Lodge and discussed the possibility of transferring my scholarship to the AHT after I had finished my Master's degree. Bob Cook clearly thought that having a free assistant had some attractions and he actively encouraged me to apply for the transfer. Interestingly, I also spent a day in each of the

Newmarket veterinary practices, which in those days had intriguingly contrasting atmospheres. I remember the imposing figure of Bob Crowhurst, who sat at the top of the very long partners' table in March House, where we discussed amongst other things, laryngeal surgery; he made it clear that his practice still relied heavily upon the experiences of Brayley Reynolds who had done some experimental laryngeal surgery during the First World War. Donald Simpson was very kind and after showing me around some of his stud farms, invited me out to lunch.

At Beaufort Cottage Stables, I met Michael Hunt who wore a bucket hat and an old sweater with a hole in it. He was absolutely charming and more like someone about to go on a fishing trip than my image of a typical Newmarket equine practitioner. Colin Peace, who was then the practice surgeon, invited me home for tea, which as he was catering for himself that evening, was cheese on toast. We discussed how difficult it might be for a young person to find a job in equine practice. However, neither of us could have imagined in April 1977, that within a couple of years he would have left his practice for a job in Canada; nor even more improbably, that within 5 years I would be employed as the practice surgeon and subsequently his successor in the partnership!

I went back to Glasgow and completed my Master's degree. I also discussed with the Levy Board the possibility of moving my scholarship to the AHT. They were very supportive but indicated that it would be up to the AHT to make the final decision. Having initially been very encouraging, Bob Cook rang me out of the blue in the late summer to inform me that he had accepted a professorship at the University of Illinois. He explained that my impending move, and as I saw it my whole future, depended upon support from the then director of the ERS, Dr Richard Archer.

In those days, I knew nothing of the politics of the Animal Health Trust. However, I was soon to discover that in this tranquil part of Suffolk, veterinary politics engendered deep passions. I contacted Dr Archer by telephone and was told very brusquely that there would be absolutely no point in my coming to the AHT, as without guidance from Bob Cook I could not possibly hope to continue to provide a second opinion service for equine respiratory disease. I had no idea that the AHT had just undergone major

restructuring. As a cost-cutting exercise, the head office in London was to be moved to Lanwades Park, Newmarket, and the jobs of director of small animal services and the director of equine research had been amalgamated into a single new post, director of the Animal Health Trust. Dr Archer had been an unsuccessful applicant and undoubtedly was very bitter about things. He clearly did not envisage a glorious future for the ERS, and certainly appeared little concerned about the future of a postgraduate student from Scotland, about whom he knew virtually nothing. Perhaps understandably, I was devastated. However, I telephoned Bob Cook, who was very sympathetic and advised me to contact Brian Singleton, the newly appointed director of the AHT.

Mike Scott and the Queen in the immunogenetics laboratory after Her Majesty opened the virology unit in 1980.

I telephoned Brian almost immediately and was greatly encouraged to hear that he thought there was every reason for my proposed transfer to go ahead. He suggested that Leo Jeffcott and Chris Colles might like to take me under their wing. Furthermore, I would spend my first few months at the heel of Bob Cook, who would be delighted to set me on the correct path. So a new phase of my career began in early October 1977, when I moved into one of the bedsit flats at the top of Balaton Lodge itself. I spent the first three months with notebook in hand, literally recording every pearl of wisdom shed by Bob Cook, who was most generous with his help and advice. Together we made several trips, including to Oxford to see Dr Gordran Ardran, who was the acknowledged medical guru on the fluoroscopic examination of swallowing, the topic of my proposed Fellowship project. I remember two things about that trip. Firstly, Ardran was a chain smoker of untipped cigarettes, which I thought quite astonishing in a person who must have examined more cancerous throats and chests of heavy smokers than almost anyone else alive! Secondly, as we drove through the centre of the beautiful city of Oxford, Bob announced rather randomly that it was a most romantic city in which to entertain a young lady. I copied this suggestion down in my notebook along with numerous pieces of invaluable advice about the equine upper airway!

Not only was Bob very kind, but Leo and Chris were most supportive and I really felt I was in a very privileged position looking at top class horses as a second opinion, when I knew that I would never have been allowed anywhere near them as a first opinion in practice. However, in a relatively novel specialism, it seemed more important that I had access to the latest technology of the day, such as fibreoptic endoscopy, good radiographic equipment including fluoroscopy, and to state of the art operating and anaesthetic recovery facilities. Even more important was the backing of more experienced veterinary and scientific colleagues, and of course of the support staff in the various departments at both Balaton Lodge and Lanwades Park. It was a wonderful place in which to learn my trade.

The Princess Royal views an electron microscopic image with Barry Allen (left) Katherine Whitwell (right) and Jenny Mumford (second from right) looking on.

Bob went to America and we corresponded regularly for several years afterwards. Very artistic and with the most beautiful handwriting, he was actually a very accomplished glass engraver. His notes were also full of marvellous drawings made during clinical and endoscopic examinations of patients. Bob had kept a number of prized specimens in an old bath full of formalin, which survived for a number of years after his departure, despite the understandable criticism of members of the pathology department. However, the quid pro quo for my opportunity at the AHT was to keep him up to date with the things which he had encouraged me to follow up, including the dissection of some rather unpleasant but interesting relics in the formalin bath!

The Animal Health Trust in the late 1970s seemed a very happy place in which to work. We initiated a number of social activities including a cricket team, and we also held an annual summer barbecue and disco at Lanwades Hall, which was always well attended by the staff and their friends. Brian was well respected and liked by his staff, and he very firmly believed that he must lead from the front. This he did in what I considered to be an energetic and coherent manner at a most critical time in its history. He lived in a flat at the top of Lanwades Hall. Not having ridden a horse for more than 25 years he acquired a chesnut mare, Rosie, which he had tacked up for him and rode out early every morning dressed in a pair of ancient jodphurs, before starting work. I felt that I developed an excellent working relationship with him, and he was undoubtedly a major influence during the early part of my professional career. However, he was certainly not a man to cross, and I did fall foul of his anger on one notable occasion.

I used to enjoy a round of golf at Newmarket Links, and Brian had asked me to ensure that a group of farriers was given the "five star" tour of Balaton Lodge on one Saturday morning. I had often shown round guests of one sort or another, as a charity it was always expected that you would put on a good show for PR purposes. However, on this particular Saturday morning I was due to play in a relatively important match, so I delegated the tour to a junior colleague. I had thought nothing more about the matter until the following Monday morning when I was hauled in front of the director. Unfortunately things had not gone at all well during the tour; the person upon which I had dumped this weekend chore had an extremely quiet voice and was unused to public speaking. Worst of all, the "group of farriers" turned out to be the Master and Wardens of the Worshipful Company of Farriers and their wives; the director was anything but impressed and left me in no doubt about it. I never made the same mistake again!

The Animal Health Trust built a new virology unit, which was opened by Her Majesty the Queen in the summer of 1981. About 18 months previously, I had been very fortunate operating on one of her pregnant broodmares, bleeding from a guttural pouch mycosis. After ligating an internal carotid artery, she had made a spectacular recovery and then delighted her owner by producing a fine colt foal. The Queen had very generously invited me to a small luncheon party at the Jockey Club, which as a relatively recent veterinary graduate I found an awe-inspiring experience. At the official opening I had been asked to chaperone a few local dignitaries including Peter Rossdale, there with his wife, Jill. I hardly knew Peter, but during a brief conversation he commented that there was nothing I was doing at the AHT, which could not be carried out as well or even better in his private practice; the suggestion registered in my mind.

In the autumn of 1981 I contacted Peter Rossdale and was eventually summoned to meet the partners. They all appeared very enthusiastic about working in Newmarket equine practice and seemed prepared to take a chance on my joining the practice. I remember Ray Hopes enquiring whether I felt I was a competent surgeon; to which I think I replied that I was a very fast learner! On December 31st I completed my Fellowship thesis and on January 1st 1982 I found myself operating on another case of guttural pouch mycosis at Beaufort Cottage Stables, under the keen eye of all five partners. I thought it a little unusual to have all five in attendance on a New Year's morning, but then I suppose I hadn't yet really prepared myself for the massive commitment that working in a Newmarket practice entailed. However, I very rapidly learnt what that meant.

My departure from the AHT was marred only by a visit from Bob Crowhurst, who felt that my joining the "opposition" was unacceptable behaviour. The tenor of his argument was that as his practice had referred numerous cases to the ERS my joining Rossdales was not only an act of disloyalty, but also to their potential commercial disadvantage. After visiting me he had an appointment with Brian Singleton. However, Brian had advised that joining Peter Rossdale was the very best career move that I could make, and he dismissed Bob Crowhurst's complaint in what I later heard was a most robust manner! Nevertheless, even 24 years after Peter had first set up his plate, there was still tension in Newmarket High Street. I was particularly sad because I had made good friends with several of the veterinary surgeons in Bob's practice and for a number of years afterwards their response to me was distinctly cool.

As I write this some thirty years later, I feel that the relationship between the two main Newmarket practices has never been more cordial. Time seems to heal all wounds.

Robert Cook FRCVS, PhD Professor of Surgery Emeritus Tufts Cummings School of Veterinary Medicine.

Dean and Professor of Veterinary Clinical Studies, Clinical Veterinary Medicine, University of Cambridge 1991-2004. Dean of the Faculty of Veterinary Science University of Sydney 2004-2009. Sub-Dean for the Camden Campus, University of Sydney, Veterinary Teaching Hospital, January 2010 - date.

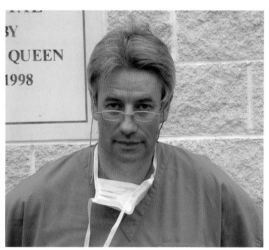

Professor Tim Greet. Current president of World Equine Veterinary Association (WEVA) and past president British Veterinary Association (BEVA).

Chapter 9

The Development of Farriery

by: Simon Curtis FWCF Hon Assoc RCVS

*S*imon Curtis was born in Newmarket and has practiced as a farrier in the town for almost 40 years. He is a fellow of the Worshipful Company of Farriers by examination and an Honorary Associate of the Royal College of Veterinary Surgeons. He has published in veterinary journals in the UK and USA and written three textbooks for vets and farriers. Simon has been Master of the Worshipful Company of Farriers (2001-2) and Chairman of the Farriers Registration Council (2006-9). He has lectured and demonstrated the subject of farriery in all six continents and continues to shoe horses in Newmarket.

Mr Bowles the veterinarian mentioned twice in the Veterinarian of 1831 was held in high regard by the racing world in Newmarket as was an unidentified 'old farrier' in the town. Mr Bowles had a forge at his Cambridge practice but was probably not directly involved in farriery at Newmarket. The term farrier at that time meant "horse doctor". The Royal Veterinary College founded 40 years previously had been trying to eradicate the title for some time. The College wanted, as the editorial illustrated, the term farrier to disappear and with it the untrained and unexamined people who used it. The horse doctor/ farrier has disappeared, although farriers in the army still dress wounds and assist the veterinary surgeon officers in many treatments.

In the same period the techniques and approaches have evolved in collaboration with, rather than opposition to, veterinary practice. This collaboration between the professions has developed, especially in the last decade.

For many years those of us who applied shoes to racehorses called ourselves farriers when all around us called us blacksmiths. This stretches across the English speaking world. The influence of the Royal College in eradicating the term farrier even stretched to the Worshipful Company of Farriers. This ancient livery company was formed in 1356 and is still the livery company of choice for both veterinary surgeons and those who shoe horses. In 1890 the WCF, having tried and failed to obtain compulsory registration for all who shod horses, embarked on a voluntary

examination. The Registered Shoeing Smith exam (RSS) became a recognised and valued standard and continues to this day as the Diploma of the Worshipful Company of Farriers (DipWCF). It only changed its name in 1975 with the advent of the Farriers Registration Act and fulfilment of the desire for compulsory registration. Some older farriers; they would now have to be 50, have the post-nominals RSS; but what a strange title - shoeing smith. No farrier I have ever known has used this term. It satisfied the WCF's need not to use the term blacksmith; there is a Worshipful Company of Blacksmiths, they forge iron, and the RCVS's need to avoid the dreaded term "farrier". Nowadays we can use the term farrier without triggering the sort of reaction that occurred in days gone by.

The words blacksmith and farrier are both ancient. Blacksmith is Anglo-Saxon, meaning to smite iron and farrier comes from ferrum which is Latin for iron. Not so different after all. Farriers in France are called le marechal ferrant. Marechal means servant of the horse or one who is in charge of the horse and led to our term Marshall, an important person indeed.

It seems that the farriers, without coming full circle, have at least returned to having an involvement in the treatment of some conditions of the horse, all-be-it just the lower leg. After the success of the RSS exam in 1890 the WCF instigated the Associate examination, aimed entirely at the use of farriery skills, i.e., foot trimming shoe-making and shoeing, for the treatment of conditions, diseases, and injuries of the leg and foot of the horse.

In the very secretive world, that was Newmarket in the early 19th century, there would have been men employed to trim and shoe the horses. There are plenty of hooves from horses of that time preserved and turned into trophies and inkwells. They are shod in the style of the day. Many with beautifully hand crafted shoes of iron; steel and aluminium did not appear until the end of the 19th century. One of the earliest recorded blacksmith/farriers was one Richard Curtis who died in 1727. Whether he is an ancestor of this author I cannot say but my family was certainly shoeing horses in the Six Mile Bottom/Wilbraham area, 5 miles to the south of Newmarket just over one hundred years later.

My Grandfather, Oliver known as Jack, was a farrier in the 1920s and was shoeing in Newmarket in the '30s. My father Don, born in 1923 left the town to serve an apprenticeship in Banbury, Oxon before the war. When called up he chose to join as a blacksmith in the Guard's Armoured Division where he mended the tank tracks. He preferred that to the shoeing of army horses where he would have been directed by the farrier sergeant; a fate he only avoided by being closer to the front line.

Soon after the war Don Curtis returned to Newmarket and in 1947 bought the forge in Moulton Road from Ted Honeybun and was joined there first by his father Jack and eventually by his brothers Russell, Peter and Maurice. The business was called O A Curtis & Sons and thrived as racing in Newmarket grew in the 1950s and 60s. There was at that time another family forge in Newmarket. Wotton's was located in Exning Road, just up from the Five Bells on the right. They were there until the middle of the 1970s and were blacksmiths and welding fabricators as well as farriers. One farrier employed by them was a certain Ron Ware but more of him later.

The Curtis forge shod racehorses at their stables during the mornings and travelled to a number of the stud farms in the afternoons. In the stables the farrier's role was to keep the horses well shod in steel and plate with aluminium the day before racing. Work on the stud was, as it still is, mainly trimming the hooves to maintain their shape and soundness. Farriers not on a stud made horseshoes in the forge which by the 1960s had 13 fires and anvils. When they were all in use the heat and noise was quite something to behold.

The author hand forging a Heart Bar shoe.

These farriers, and others in the town, were fulfilling the main functions of a farrier; to trim excess growth, to protect from wear, and to give grip. At some point the farrier's expertise must have been used for remedial purposes in conjunction with a vet. This is not a new idea; Fiachi's treatise of 1556 is the earliest recorded work by a veterinary surgeon on the use of a farrier's skills to cure lameness. A library of books were written on this subject, reaching a peak in the mid 19th century. They were mainly written by veterinary surgeons for farriers. In 1977 John Hickman, the renowned veterinary surgeon published Farriery, still the main textbook for training farriers in the UK today.

The quote in the title page is as follows: *"A proper mode of shoeing is certainly of more importance than the treatment of any disease, or perhaps of all the diseases incident to horses. The foot is the part that we are particularly required to preserve in health: and if this art be judiciously employed, the foot will not be more liable to disease than any other region."* He was quoting Edward Coleman, 1765-1839, the second principal of the Royal Veterinary College.

An Egg Bar shoe.

My boyhood recollections of visiting studfarms and stables with my father, in the mid 1960s, were of him working on individual horses with particular problems. Occasionally there was a vet there and a meeting with the manager of the stud or trainer. It seemed normal to me, as a 12 year old, but it is obvious now that these were referrals for more than a normal trim or shoeing. By that time he was travelling overseas to teach in such exotic places as Brazil, Turkey and Hong Kong, usually at the invitation of vets associated with those countries respective Jockey Clubs. It seemed perfectly natural to me that farriers and vets worked alongside each other for the betterment of the horse. Such is the naivety of youth!

I started my apprenticeship in 1972 and would sometimes assist my father with a case. On one occasion he had trimmed a foal's foot for the reception of a tip (shoe) and returned to the forge to make the tip. A shoe of no more than 7cm across, with accurate nail-holes for the tiny foot. Then back to the stud to nail it on. On placing it on

the foot, I could see his face, first mystified then angry. "Someone has interfered with this foot", he stated. "Our vet", came the reply, "he thought it needed a little more off, so he trimmed it", was added defensively. Don placed the shoe outside the stable and we left. "He can nail it on for you then", were his last words on the subject.

His inspiration to me was that even when 60 he believed there must be better ways to shoe and treat equine feet. He was always experimenting with different hoof-wear, glues and materials. He recognised that farriery could be used to bring about beneficial changes to the horse beyond the foot, that we can especially affect the conformation of a foal in it's formative months. Shoeing a foal by nailing is no mean feat for even an accomplished farrier, without the sedatives of today it was simply the highest example of the farrier's skill.

After 10 years as a farrier I was looking for a little more in my career and discovered that right on my doorstep the science of farriery was being pushed forward by two vets and a farrier at the Equine Research Station (now the Animal Health Trust, AHT) less than a mile from our forge. There at Ballaton Lodge, vets Chris Colles and Sven Kold were working with farrier Ron Ware just on lame horses. Referred from all over the country, all types and breeds were coming to the forge to be shod. Sven Kold, introduced the Egg bar shoe to the UK. A shoe rediscovered (after 2000 years they have all been made before) by Ostblom, a vet from Sven's native Denmark. A shoe to treat navicular disease. What a revelation to me; a disease that has caused such losses in the sporting horse world, treated not with medicine or an operation but by a farrier with a horseshoe. Colles published his famous paper on "Foot Balance" and Ron Ware was invited to speak at the British Equine Veterinary Association Congress to a packed house.

In 1984 I won a national Farriery award for my paper, *"The Foal to Three Year Old: Problems Experienced by the Farrier."* My prize was to travel to the Equine Veterinary Hospital in Helsingborg, Sweden. There were a dozen vets there and 4 farriers. The farrier's duties rotated so that they spent time in the forge, assisting in the operating theatre and other parts of the hospital. It was the first time that I had ventured into a theatre and I was struck by the informality but strong mutual respect all involved had.

By the 1980s I was frequently called into Beaufort Cottage stables by some of the partners and assistants of the Rossdale Partnership. There had been much publicity, around that time, with regard to the technique of dorsal wall resection and the application of Heart Bar shoes for the treatment of laminitis. I was desperate to try my hand at this but as a vet had been struck off for the incorrect use of this treatment (the horse was subjected to euthanasia), the vets were not as keen. One day, Rob Pilsworth, a young assistant, called me to the practice and asked my opinion on a laminitis case. I of course, suggested that it was an ideal case for a resection and shoeing with Heart Bars. He agreed and said he would be back in an hour. He had left the x-rays, taken specifically for me to work, and on which we had agreed the plan.

When he returned his only words were, *"Bloody hell, I didn't think you would take that much off!"* Not a drop off blood had been spilt but the whole dorsal wall of the front hooves was gone, exposing the dead detached laminae. Tim Greet, one of the partners walked by, took one look and said *"If I did that I would be struck off!"* I did point out that as I was on practice premises, working in agreement with one of his assistants, he could still be struck off. The horse went from strength to strength and showed a remarkable improvement and we started to use the technique on many cases.

We had a great run of successes, with Tim and I working on many cases. Eventually though we had two failures, both put down on the same day. It brought home to me that there is no infallible treatment and using farriery to treat horses was different from just shoeing and trimming. Never-the-less I was able to try new techniques under the umbrella of a veterinary practice with their full support, providing I could convince them of the rationale.

Tim Greet asked me to look at a horse called Dallas, trained by Luca Cumani. He was lame from a crack to one of his front hooves that bled at exercise. I had occasionally seen quarter-cracks as they are called but considered them mainly an American problem. With the hotter summers of the 90s and the advent of synthetic gallops, they became our problem as well. I had no method of repairing cracks but I recognised an imbalance and knew that a bar shoe would help stabilise the hoof capsule. So after a discussion with Tim and the trainer, that was the agreed treatment. Cumani also

muttered that a sound Dallas would win the Cambridgeshire; the great handicap in the autumn. I went and had a bet at 25-1. I hand-made aluminium plates and they were welded at the local fabricator. Steel is easy to weld, aluminium not so. Dallas won the Cambridgeshire that year carrying an all time record weight and I began a lifetime interest in the causes and cures of hoof-cracks.

Aluminium caudal extensions glued to a foal with flaccid tendons.

By 1995 we finally had a glue that, when correctly applied, would firmly attach a shoe to a hoof. Acrylics have quite extraordinary strength and will attach aluminium to horn far more securely than any nail. This was the biggest advance in farriery for 2,000 years and an opportunity to achieve that which had been difficult or impossible previously. I had had in mind attaching heel extensions to foals for many years and now had the means. I was asked by Sarah Stoneham if I could do anything for a foal referred to the practice, with severe hypoflexion (flaccid) tendons of the hind limbs. I fashioned aluminium strips 5cm wide by 20cm long and stuck them with the new glue. The foal was walked for 10mins three times a day and within the month the shoes were off and the foal resumed a normal life. The case was published in Equine Veterinary Education the next year by Sarah and me. This technique has spread around the world and is still the chosen method for treating this condition.

In 2002 I was made an Honorary Associate of the Royal College of Veterinary Surgeons. I was the 56th person in 85 years to receive it and am still the only farrier. The citation said that I had advanced veterinary knowledge and brought together veterinary surgeons and farriers for the benefit of the horse. I like to think that there is some mutual benefit as well.

A painting of Charles Vial de St Bel showing him instructing a shoeing smith. Ignorance is seen fleeing. Reproduced by kind permission The Royal Veterinary College.

The Greenwood Ellis (now Newmarket Equine Hospital, NEH) practice in Newmarket began employing my brother Nick Curtis on an ad hoc basis in the 1990s and Mark Rose took over from Ron Ware at the AHT. They had moved out of town to Kennett and built a new forge. Rossdales had created the Diagnostic Centre in Exning and I finally had a forge and facilities to shoe. Previously at Beaufort Cottage Stables I had used the prep room for the operating theatre to shoe in; which was never ideal. The NEH was built in 2009 with a designated room for the farrier. Now in Newmarket there are three equine hospitals all with a dedicated forge and a number of farriers interested in working with vets to use their skills and knowledge in corrective and remedial farriery.

We may not have come full circle since 1831 when the veterinary profession felt threatened and deprived of work by 'the grooms empire' and 'an old farrier' at Newmarket. Farriers are never going to return to being "horse doctors" but more and more veterinary surgeons realise that a skilled farrier is essential in the treatment of many conditions of the leg and foot of the horse. Equally, many farriers are pushing themselves to acquire the additional knowhow to deal with these cases.

References:
The Changing Face of Newmarket 1600- 1760, Peter May

Trattao Dell Imbriglare, Attegiare, e Farrare`cavilli, 1556

John Hickman, Farriery, J A Allen, London, 1977

Simon's great grandfather Oliver Curtis with his son Oliver.

Simon rasping a horse's foot.

Seventeenth century horse shoe found at the National Stud in Newmarket.

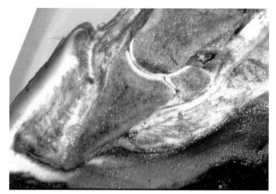

Sectioned foot of a horse with severe laminitis. The outer hoof is seperated from the pedal bone by chronic inflammatory tissue (pedal rotation).

Chapter 10

The Equine Fertility Unit

by: Peter Rossdale OBE PhD FRCVS

The Equine Fertility Unit was established in the early 1970's with the object of improving fertility rates in horses, particularly in Thoroughbreds. Its origin and continuation for more than 35 years were due largely to the visionary foresight and enthusiasm of a group of scientists and horse breeders, which included Professors Roger Short FRS, W.R. (Twink) Allen ScD CBE, Thaddeus Mann CBE FRS and Peter Burrell CBE, Colonel Nat Frieze and Dr Bob Moor FRS.

The key player throughout the existence of the Unit was Twink Allen. He had graduated from Sydney Veterinary School in 1965 and having married Diana Emms returned to his home country, New Zealand, to join a large animal veterinary practice in Kaitaia, situated in the far north of the North Island. Three months later they were involved in a serious head-on car accident which put Twink in hospital in Auckland for 9 months, followed by 3 months in a rehabilitation centre learning to re-use his badly broken legs.

Dr RM (Bob) Moor.

As in all our lives chance is the major controlling influence in our destiny. For Twink, instead of continuing in practice in New Zealand, he successfully applied for a graduate post at the

Veterinary School in the University of Cambridge, in order to study for a PhD. This he did under the supervision of Dr Roger Short FRS. The study produced highly original work on Pregnant Mares' Serum Gonadotrophin (PMSG), which plays a significant role in the early stages of equine pregnancy. As a result of Twink's study, PMSG hormone is now more correctly termed equine Chorionic Gonadotrophin (eCG). Another original finding showed that the cells within the equine endometrial cups in the pregnant horn of the mare's uterus are fetal and not maternal as previously thought.

Embryo transfers in ponies of donkey, zebra, Przewalski.

Twink then accepted a 2-year Postdoctoral Fellowship to study equine reproduction at the world renowned Animal Research Station on the Huntington Road in Cambridge under the combined supervision of the late Tim Rowson FRS and Professor Mann FRS. It was in this way that the Equine Fertility Unit, described first as the Equine Reproduction Project, began its embryonic life. The full story is recounted in a publication obtainable from the Paul Mellon Laboratory of Equine Reproduction, currently housed at Brunswick, 18 Woodditton Road, Newmarket CB8 9BJ. In the book, Allen describes the early days of the Unit as follows:

"The Fellowship to work on horse reproduction at the Animal Research Station had been cobbled together with various bits of money by the late Peter Burrell CBE, doyen of the British turf, Director of the British National Stud for over 30 years and architect of the newly created National Stud in Newmarket. As Chairman of the Thoroughbred Breeders' Association at the time,

Peter was sufficiently wise and far-sighted to be concerned that any new infection which might arise in Thoroughbreds and prevent mating during the covering season could be financially disastrous for the industry; indeed, he accurately presaged the outbreak of Contagious Equine Metritis (CEM) which did just that in Newmarket 7 years later in 1977 (Simpson and Eaton-Evans, 1978). Hence, he established the Equine Reproduction Project at the Animal Research Station to investigate the feasibility and practical difficulties of establishing a deep frozen semen bank for all the major Thoroughbred stallions in Britain, to use in conjunction with artificial insemination (AI) in the event of a disease outbreak preventing the free movement of horses during the covering season."

Mertoun Paddocks.

The EFU became a pioneer in the subject of embryo transfer which, in the 1970's, was quite commonplace in cattle but not at all in horses. The work at the Unit threw further light on the understanding of equine fertility in that following ovulation the embryo does not enter the uterus until 6 days later where it moves continually throughout the internal surface of that organ over the next 10 days.,

Some years later, the EFU Senior Research Associate, Dr Sandra Wilsher, produced a novel and simple method for non-surgical embryo transfer using a speculum to expand the vagina and thereby allow the use of special forceps to enable easy and smooth passage of a larger pipette via which the embryo could be transferred into the uterus.

Under Allen's auspices the Unit developed a close collaborative relationship with the equine veterinary practices in Newmarket and elsewhere. The practical aspects of this collaboration included

the pioneering use of prostaglandin to induce estrous by its effect on the progesterone secreting yellow body (corpus luteum) in the mare's ovary. In contrast, another new treatment was the orally active progestagen, allyl trembolone, subsequently traded under the name of Regumate. This, together with improved knowledge and use of artificial lighting during winter darkness greatly improved the efficiency of inducing fertile oestrous periods in mares during the early part of the mating season. i.e late February, March and early April in the Northern hemisphere. .

Michael Wates CBE, Nat Frieze & Peter Willett.

The EFU's introduction of ultrasound scanning of the mare's ovaries and uterus was a major milestone for veterinary practice. The original work was performed in collaboration with Dr Eric Palmer at INRA in France and it led to the manufacture of ultrasound machines designed specifically for use on mares reproductive organs and which became routine for veterinary practice worldwide.

It is perhaps in the field of immunology, as between that of the mare and her fetus during pregnancy, that the EFU made the most notable scientific advances. This was achieved in the form of between-species embryo transfers. The work was supported by a longstanding and much valued collaborator and Honorary Member of the EFU, Professor Doug Antczak, and his team at the Equine Immunogenitics Laboratory of Cornell University Veterinary School. Donkey-in- horse, horse-in-donkey, horse and donkey-in- mule and zebra-in-horse pregnancies were all established.

90

These results threw significant light on the immunological mechanisms operating to prevent the mare rejecting her fetal foal as a foreign body. Scientific work of this nature is notoriously difficult to perform and even more problematical in establishing direct relationship with the studies undertaken in practice; this both in medical and veterinary worlds. However, the work performed at the EFU provided a piece in the complicated jigsaw of understanding equine reproduction and made a valuable basis for further work by which the findings can be applied in practice for the benefit of the horse and their breeders.

Professor Roger Short FRS.

In 1989 the EFU was translocated to Newmarket when the 114 acre Mertoun Paddocks which was rented from the Duke of Sutherland's Stetchworth Estate through the auspices of Peter Burrell. The Unit continued its work once established in Newmarket. Its staff and collaborators included a series of distinguished scientists and postgraduate students studying for their PhDs.. Identical twins were created by splitting embryos which provided unique material for study of the horse genome.

In 1986 a generous donation from the late Jim Joel's Childwick Trust established a Professorship of Equine Reproduction for Twink in the Department of Clinical Veterinary Medicine at the University of Cambridge. This provided tenure for Allen and much needed academic stability and kudos for the EFU. It opened up a wealth of collaborative opportunities with other University research departments and groups. The Unit thus provided a unique practical teaching facility for Cambridge veterinary students.

In the book describing the history of the EFU, Allen concludes that the 7 years of the New Millennium could be summarised by the words Statue, Barker hypothesis *(re growth retardation in the uterus)*, Cloning, Stem cells and Closure. The statue took the form of the Newmarket stallion with handler erected as a Millennium project on the large Stetchworth Toll roundabout at the southern entrance to Newmarket opposite the entrances to the National Stud and July racecourse.

Opening of Unit by Her Majesty, April 1989, with the Director Professor Allen. Sam Shepherd in the background.

The hypothesis put forward by Professor Barker referred to the work undertaken to test and explain the problem of the dysmature foal; that is, the foal that suffers disadvantages during pregnancy due to relative incompetence of the maturational process caused by deficiencies of the maternal, placental or fetal processes of development. Professor Barker, the original pioneer of this process in human infants, gave his name to the syndrome.

Cloning and the production of unique equine

embryonic stem cells were other ventures undertaken at the Unit in the New Millenium until closure in 2007 was effected on Twink's retirement from the Cambridge Chair by the TBA on the grounds of insufficient funding. This decision, claimed by many as being shortsighted, was much regretted by those in the veterinary and horsebreeding communities who appreciated the importance of the work performed at the EFU and its unique facility for research devoted to the specialist subject of equine reproduction.

Tim Rowson FRS and Albert Stakemire.

Millenium Newmarket Sculpt by Marcia Astor.

Professor Thaddeus Mann.

Artist's impression of view of Newmarket from Warren Hill. Peter Williams oil.

John Winter's string about to leave Highfields stables, Bury Road, for the morning exercise. Oil painting by Peter Williams.

Competitor going to start on the July Course, Newmarket. Mares on the National Stud in background. Photo by courtesy Trevor Jones.

Horses in training sale at Tattersalls Newmarket. Photo by courtesy Trevor Jones.

The Statue sculpted by Marcia Astor at the entrances to the July Course and National Stud. December 2009. Photo by courtesy Trevor Jones.

The Fox at Tattersalls. Photo by courtesy Trevor Jones.

Goodbye! Photo by courtesy Trevor Jones.

Stanley House Stables in the seventies when Bernard van Cutsem trained there, including Park Top. Peter Williams oil.

Frankel, winner of the 2000 guineas. Bred and owned by K. Abdullah (Juddmonte), trained by Sir Henry Cecil and ridden by Tom Queally. Photo by courtesy Trevor Jones.

Newmarket Rowley Mile stands. Photo by courtesy Trevor Jones.

Horses on way to the Heath. Photo by courtesy Trevor Jones.

Illustrators contributing to the book

James Power was born in 1946 and now lives and works at the heart of the British Horse Racing community in Newmarket where he has been Senior Stud Groom at Banstead Manor. James is an accomplished professional painter, working in oils, watercolours and pastels.. He is an active member of the Society of Equestrian Artists. Promoted to Associate Member in 2000, and to Full Member in 2001, James is a past member of the Society's Executive Committee. He has been a major prize winner and, in 1998, one of his works was adjudged 'Best Racing Picture' for 'Horse and Hound' magazine.

Trevor Jones lives near Newmarket and is a world-renowned sport photographer who has spent the past two decades creating the Thoroughbred Photography's Comprehensive Library of thousands of beautiful, brilliant horse racing images. In this enterprise he was building on the techniques and experience gathered during his years as a sports photographer in Fleet Street and working for top sports photo agencies, covering a host of international sports events for very demanding clients, Trevor has sought to capture the photogenic elegance and athleticism of the thoroughbred racehorse and its environment.

Peter Williams was born in 1934 in New Zealand. Originally a sheep and cattle farmer his painting success in New Zealand and Australia led to an invitation by Qantas Airlines to join their inaugural 747 flight to the USA in 1971 where he painted and exhibited travelling by motorhome with his family.Ten years later he brought his children to America again to attend art school and paint. While here Peter was commissioned to paint horse racing scenes by the Racing Scene Gallery in New York City. He has been resident artist for nearly thirty years at Churchill Downs, Keeneland, Del Mar, Saratoga and Monmouth Park. He also paints flowers, marine subjects, architecture, figure studies and vintage automobiles all from life.

John Fuller was born in 1934 and spent his childhood in Burwell a few miles from Newmarket. In his book, Fullers view from the attic, he recounts his mother's experience in the chair at a Newmarket dentist when the high street was bombed and many people lost their lives. John served in the RAF and subsequently worked in the National Agricultural Advisory Service before joining the Animal Pathology Laboratory of the University of Cambridge. He came to work on microbiology at the Veterinary School where small rooms in the attic were made available for stem cell and other endeavours. In his spare time he became an illustrator for electronic presentations by colleagues.